Fundamentals of
ELECTRIC WAVES

By HUGH HILDRETH SKILLING, Ph.D.

PROFESSOR OF ELECTRICAL ENGINEERING

STANFORD UNIVERSITY

NEW YORK

JOHN WILEY & SONS, INC.

LONDON: CHAPMAN & HALL, LIMITED

19359

PREFACE

In these days of ultra-high frequency, engineers speak familiarly of waves, wave guides, radiation, reflection, polarization, and other matters that as recently as a few months ago were considered rather academic. Then suddenly, and somewhat as a result of the war, these concepts were demanded in engineering practice. The Navy Department, for example, now recommends " Reflection and Refraction of Electric Waves " and " Antenna Design and Theory " in a training course for ensigns, and the Secretary of War says in the daily papers that " intense study is being given to the wave echoes of radio."

Because electric waves have become important to so many people, it appears timely to offer in this book the material on the subject that has been used for several years in the form of lecture notes and mimeographed syllabus. In the book, as in the lecture course, the purpose is to introduce electric waves. The principles of wave action and, in particular, the basic ideas of Maxwell's equations are presented in a way that has proved to be understandable to students, and the ideas are then discussed and used in simple examples until they become thoroughly familiar. Physical concepts are stressed, but without overlooking either mathematical rigor on one hand or engineering practice on the other. A radio engineer may thus find the book helpful in acquiring a background for understanding antenna arrays, transmission lines, wave guides, reflectors, resonators, and electromagnetic horns; and he will even come to see wave theory in the behavior of a receiving antenna or a vertical radiator for a broadcast transmitter. A physicist, having less interest in these practical uses, may find the book helpful as an introduction to some more advanced work on electromagnetic theory.

The content of the book has been used for university courses, where it is most effective at about the senior college level. It has also been presented to a group of experienced radio engineers in the Engineering, Science, and Management Defense Training program. The book is arranged for those who do not necessarily have any previous knowledge of electromagnetic theory: all that is required is general college physics and mathematics through calculus. Vector analysis is introduced for use in the book but it is not expected that the reader should have any earlier acquaintance with it.

The opening chapters of the book concern themselves with electrostatics, the use of vector analysis, and similar matters that will be discouraging to the impatient reader. To some these opening chapters will be fascinating, to others, tedious. In any case they cannot be helped, for one cannot have waves without electric and magnetic fields, nor can one understand a wave until the basic fields are thoroughly familiar.

Maxwell's equations, appearing about the middle of the book, are presented as logical conclusions of the work that has gone before. Then, with their aid, radiation and wave propagation are readily developed, and these topics lead to a short discussion of antennas, transmission lines, and wave guides.

Problems are given with each chapter, and they are an integral part of the book. Most of them supplement some idea that is left without complete discussion in the text. They are arranged in the same order as the text material with which they are to be used, and in general one or two of them should be worked day by day. Also — and this is very important — many of the concepts of the book are new to the reader and will cease to seem strange only after continued and repeated use. Abraham and Becker, at the beginning of the examples in their *Classical Electricity and Magnetism*, refer the student to James 1 : 22; I cannot think of any better advice.

Preparation of this book has left me indebted to many people. First is Hazel Dillon Skilling, my wife, whose name should properly appear on the title page as coauthor, except that she will not have it so.

Stanford University has a farsighted and generous policy that encourages publication, and the opportunity to prepare this book is owing to Dr. F. E. Terman, head of the department of electrical engineering, Dean Samuel B. Morris, and Chancellor Ray Lyman Wilbur.

The general method of presentation of material in the book follows a course formerly given at the Massachusetts Institute of Technology by Dr. M. S. Vallarta. It was a course with distinction and character, of which I hope a little may be reflected in the book.

For technical aid I have borrowed from many authors. A number of the reference works I have used are given in the bibliography, which is partly an acknowledgment, and partly a suggestion of the kind of books and periodicals to which the reader may refer. The list is by no means complete; in mathematics and basic science, particularly, it merely names, in each field, the book I chanced to use. But I hope it will be an aid in finding references to use with this book and in later study.

HUGH HILDRETH SKILLING

Stanford University
July, 1942

CONTENTS

CHAPTER I

EXPERIMENTS ON THE ELECTROSTATIC FIELD

FIELDS. The study of electricity commonly begins with electric circuit theory. Current is considered to flow in a wire, being driven through resistance, inductance, and capacitance by the appropriate voltages. This is the natural approach to the subject, for electric circuits are tangible and to most people they are reasonably familiar.[1] The historical development of the subject, however, was quite the opposite: magnetic and electrostatic *fields* were well understood before circuit theory was developed — before even Ohm's law was discovered. Logically, also, as will later be seen, circuit theory may be considered as a special case of the more general theory of electromagnetic fields.

There are various kinds of fields. There are vector fields and scalar fields. A gravitational field, for example, is a vector field. Consider the gravitational field within a room. If an object of unit mass were placed at any point of space within the room there would be a force upon it. This is a particularly simple example of a field of force, for in it the force is practically the same at every point within the room; it is the same in magnitude and vertically downward in direction. It is a *vector* field, for it is not fully defined until it is known at all points in both magnitude and direction.

Fields of force are always vector fields. A *scalar* field may be illustrated by temperature. A temperature field would be determined if one were to measure the temperature at each point in a room with a thermometer. There is a value of temperature at each point, but no direction is associated with temperature. The temperature field is therefore a *scalar* field.

Electric and magnetic fields are vector fields. The electrostatic field will be considered first, for it is in some ways the simplest.

EXPERIMENT I. *The Electric Field.* It is found by experiment that there is a field of force about any object that has an electric charge. This field of force is made evident when an exploring particle that carries on itself a small electric charge is placed at some point in the region near the charged body. If it is placed at point *a* in Fig. 1, there is a

[1] This approach is used in *Transient Electric Currents*, H. H. Skilling, McGraw-Hill Book Co., New York, 1937.

1

force $\mathbf{F}_a$; at points b and c there are forces $\mathbf{F}_b$ and $\mathbf{F}_c$. If the charge on the exploring particle is changed, force upon the particle changes in proportion. This experiment, which will be called Experiment I,

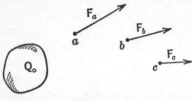

FIG. 1

makes it possible to give the following definition of the electrostatic field.

By definition, the **electrostatic field strength** at each point is equal in magnitude and direction to the force exerted on a small exploring particle carrying unit charge of positive electricity that is at rest at that point.

Symbolically,

$$\mathbf{F} = \alpha Q \mathbf{E} \qquad [1]$$

where $\mathbf{F}$ and $\mathbf{E}$ are force and electric field strength, respectively, and Q is the charge on the exploring particle. Note that this equation is not limited to any one point, but applies at *all* points. It is therefore a *field* equation, and since it relates both magnitude and direction it is a *vector* field equation.

UNITS. The quantity α is merely a factor of proportionality, and its value depends on the units used. The subject of units and dimensions is a fascinating one. It is made extremely complex by the fact that almost every author introduces a few changes to suit his personal preference. It is not possible or desirable to discuss the subject fully in this book,[2] but a short review will be helpful.

The " practical " system of electrical units, including the volt, the ampere, and the ohm, is the most familiar. This is extended by the MKS (*meter-kilogram-second*) or *Giorgi* system to include magnetic and mechanical units, and so becomes a comprehensive system based on units of practical size. Various international conferences have approved this system[3] (although without agreement on certain questions that arise) and it has many excellent features. It appears that it may be widely adopted, particularly by electrical engineers.

[2 For an excellent summary see " Physical Units and Standards " by Ernst Weber, Section 3 of *Handbook of Engineering Fundamentals*, John Wiley & Sons, New York, 1936.

[3] " I.E.C. Adopts MKS System of Units," Arthur E. Kennelly, *Trans. AIEE*, volume 54, 1935, pages 1373–1384.

" Recent Developments in Electrical Units," Arthur E. Kennelly, *Electrical Engineering*, volume 58, February, 1939, pages 78–80.

" Revision of Electrical Units," E. C. Crittenden, *Electrical Engineering*, volume 59, April, 1940, pages 160–163.

The " electromagnetic " and the " electrostatic " systems of units are commonly learned in introductory college courses in electrical physics. The former is convenient for solving magnetic problems, the latter for electrostatic work. Both use mechanical units of the CGS (*centimeter-gram-second*) system. It is rather common to give names to units in the electromagnetic system similar to names of the corresponding "practical" units but with the prefix *ab-*, as *abvolts* and *abohms*, and to name units in the electrostatic system with the prefix *stat-*, as *statvolts* and *statohms*.

The more commonly used units of both the electromagnetic and electrostatic systems are combined in the Gaussian or " symmetric " system. This system has the advantage of simplifying electromagnetic equations, particularly those relating to waves, and much of the literature of electromagnetic theory therefore uses Gaussian units.

The Gaussian units of electricity are identical with " electrostatic " units (the *statvolt, statampere, statohm,* etc.); the Gaussian units of magnetism are those of the " electromagnetic " system (the *oersted, gauss, maxwell,* and *gilbert*). CGS mechanical units are used. Hence for problems in either static electricity or magnetism the Gaussian system is similar to the familiar " electrostatic " and " electromagnetic " systems.

In the Gaussian system, however, current, as an electrical quantity, is measured in statamperes. When current appears in the same equation with magnetic units a proportionality factor, c, is required. Gaussian units will be used in this book and, beginning with Chapter VII, many of the equations will contain this constant, c. It is the ratio of one abampere to one statampere, and is numerically almost exactly 3×10^{10}.

In the Gaussian system the value of unity is assigned to both the permeability and the dielectric constant of free space[4] (vacuum).

In Table I (inside front cover) Gaussian units of electricity and magnetism are compared with electromagnetic and electrostatic CGS

[4] Systems of units are sometimes "rationalized." " Rationalization," as Crittenden says (*loc. cit.*), " means defining the units in such a way as to shift the factor of 4π, which inevitably appears in some of the equations, to places that are believed to be more logical and convenient."

When the Gaussian system is " rationalized " it becomes the Lorentz system, in which the permeability of free space is 4π and its dielectric constant $\frac{1}{4}\pi$, with corresponding changes in the other units.

In the " unrationalized " MKS system the permeability of free space is 10^{-7}, and the dielectric constant of free space is $(\frac{1}{9}) \times 10^{-9}$; the " rationalized " MKS values are $4\pi \times 10^{-7}$ and $(\frac{1}{36\pi}) \times 10^{-9}$, respectively. Which of these is preferable is one of the questions regarding the MKS system not yet settled by international conference.

units (*emu* and *esu* respectively) and with practical or *Giorgi* MKS units. There are many other systems in use, and to a large extent the system used is dependent upon the specific problem to be solved.

There are a few easily remembered relations that help to give an appreciation of the size of units in the Gaussian system. The *statvolt* is 300 volts. The *statfarad* is approximately one micromicrofarad. The *statohm* is about a million megohms. The *statampere* is 1/3000 of a microampere.

The abampere is 10 amperes, but this is not part of the Gaussian system. The *abhenry*, which is a Gaussian unit, is a millionth of a millihenry. It will be seen that the Gaussian system employs units of moderate to high voltages, extremely small currents, and therefore enormously high impedances. This is its principal disadvantage.

In the Gaussian system, as in the familiar electrostatic system, with force in dynes, α is unity and equation 1 becomes

$$\mathbf{F} = Q\mathbf{E} \qquad [2]$$

Thus the electric field is defined.

Having defined an electric field, we may study its properties. How does it arrange itself in space? For this purpose, more experimentation is necessary. Three more experiments with the exploring particle will be considered.

These experiments are not suggested as practical experiments to be done in the laboratory. They would be difficult to perform. But they are exceptionally useful experiments to serve as a foundation for theory. Let us accept, for purposes of this discussion, that the following experiments have been performed with the results given below.

EXPERIMENT II. An exploring particle, which carries a small electric charge, is moved through a region in which there is an electrostatic field. It is found that when the particle is moved in a closed path, so that it returns to the point from which it started, no total work is done either on the particle or by the particle.

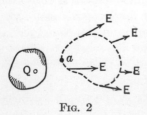

FIG. 2

In Fig. 2, for example, an exploring particle a may be moved around the path indicated by the dash line. While receding from the charged body from which the electric field radiates (as indicated by arrows, $\mathbf{E}$) work is done by the electric field upon the particle. But as the particle returns toward the charged body, following the other half of the path indicated, it must do equal work in moving against the force of the field.

It will be noted that this conclusion is in agreement with the principle of conservation of energy. If the particle returned to its initial point with an excess of energy it could go around again, and continue to go around, each time gaining a little energy without a corresponding loss of energy in another part of the system. This would make perpetual motion feasible, and is contrary to the principle of conservation of energy. It is equally impossible that the particle should return to its initial point with a deficiency of energy, for (assuming no friction) the total energy of the system would then have diminished.

The conclusion from Experiment II is entirely independent of the shape of the path followed by the exploring particle; it may be circular, elliptical, square, or any other closed path. The conclusion is also independent of the source of the electric field, which may emanate from a charged body, or from a number of charged bodies, or from a charge that is diffuse in space. The charge which produces the electric field must not change in any way while the exploring particle is making its complete circuit, for this is an electro*static* experiment, and it follows that the charge on the exploring particle must be so small that its presence does not appreciably alter the distribution of the main charge.

Since energy is equal to the product of force and distance, and the net energy is the summation, or integral, of the individual energies contributed by each increment of distance around the closed path, it follows that

$$\oint \mathbf{F} \cdot d\mathbf{s} = 0$$

Then, since the force field and the electric field are related by a constant factor, as in equation 2, we obtain

$$\oint \mathbf{E} \cdot d\mathbf{s} = 0 \qquad [3]$$

This expression is a line integral, s representing distance along the path of integration. The small circle superimposed upon the integral sign indicates that the integration is to be carried out around a *closed* path. The notation will be further explained in Chapter II.

EXPERIMENT III. A closed surface is located in space. It may be any shape: spherical, ellipsoidal, cubical, or irregular, but it must be completely closed and must not be, for example, a sphere with a hole in it. It is a purely imaginary surface, and is used only to isolate the space within from the space outside.

Let us choose the imaginary closed surface so that it does not pass through any solid or liquid material. (This is a restriction that will be removed later, but at present it simplifies the discussion.) It would be better from the theoretical point of view if the imaginary surface did not pass through any material substance, including air, but air affects the results of Experiment III by less than a tenth of a per cent and is usually negligible.

Experiment III is now performed by measuring the electric field strength (by means of an exploring particle) at every point on the closed surface. This can best be done by dividing the surface into a very large number of small sections, as in Fig. 3, each having an area *da*. The component of the electric field normal to the small area *da* is

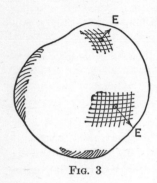

FIG. 3

then determined. If the normal component is outward it is called positive, if inward it is negative. Then all the normal components are multiplied by their respective areas, and the results added together (as in the left-hand member of equation 4). When this experiment has been tried for all possible surfaces under the widest imaginable variety of circumstances, the conclusion is reached that the summation described above will be proportional to the amount of electric charge enclosed within the surface on which measurements are made. If *h* is a constant and *Q* is the amount of charge within the surface,

$$\oint \mathbf{E} \cdot d\mathbf{a} = hQ \qquad [4]$$

This is a surface integral, **a** representing area. The small circle upon the integral sign here indicates that integration is to be carried out over a *closed* surface.

If, in Fig. 3, the summation of the normal component of **E** over the entire surface is zero, it follows that there is no electric charge within the surface or, if there is any positive charge within, there is also an equal amount of negative charge. But if the summation is not zero, there is a net electric charge within the surface, and the amount of contained charge is proportional to the summation of the electric field strength over the surface, as in equation 4. The value of the proportionality constant *h* is dependent upon the units in which *E* and *Q* are measured; in Gaussian units $h = 4\pi$ and equation 4 is (for free space):

$$\oint \mathbf{E} \cdot d\mathbf{a} = 4\pi Q \qquad [5]$$

EXPERIMENT IV. Now let us repeat Experiment III, this time taking measurements of electrostatic field strength at points on an imaginary surface in oil. As before, the field strength is measured by determining the force on a charged exploring particle, but whereas in Experiment III the charged particle was in air (or, strictly, in vacuum) now each measurement is to be made with the particle in oil. The value of the integral of equation 5, corresponding to a certain amount of electric charge within the enclosing surface, proves to be different from the value obtained when the same amount of electric charge was contained within a closed surface in air.

In petroleum oil, the experimental value obtained for the integral of equation 5 is about half the value in air. If the experiment is repeated in other substances, other different values will be found. To generalize equation 5 we assign to each substance a factor of proportionality known as its **dielectric constant,** and using the symbol κ to denote this factor the equation may be rewritten in the more general form

$$\oint \kappa \mathbf{E} \cdot d\mathbf{a} = 4\pi Q \qquad [6]$$

The factor κ is characteristic of the material in which $\mathbf{E}$ is measured, although it changes somewhat with temperature and other physical conditions. Thus for most oils that are derivatives of petroleum its value is between 2 and 2.5. In cottonseed or olive oil it is about 3. In ethyl alcohol at room temperature it is about 25, and in pure distilled water about 80.

It is not uncommon in writing equation 6 to substitute the symbol $\mathbf{D}$ for the product $\kappa \mathbf{E}$, whereupon the equation becomes

$$\oint \mathbf{D} \cdot d\mathbf{a} = 4\pi Q \qquad [7]$$

To conclude Experiment IV we make measurements on surfaces that pass through various different substances. The experimental result is that equation 6 is correct even though its surface of integration lies in different or non-homogeneous materials. Thus the surface may be partly in air and partly in oil, and the equation as stated is still valid.

The results of these experiments are easily visualized in terms of electrostatic flux. Flux lines give the direction of the electric field. Moreover, the lines are so drawn that each one represents a certain extent of electric field. If, for example, an electric field of strength E is uniform over a plane surface, and is perpendicular to the surface, as in Fig. 4, the number of lines of flux passing through the surface is found by multiplying the field strength E by the area of the surface and by the dielectric constant of the material.

If the electric field is not normal to the surface, flux is equal to the product of the area, the dielectric constant, and the *normal component* of the field. In the extreme case, with field parallel to the surface, there is no normal component and no flux penetrates the surface.

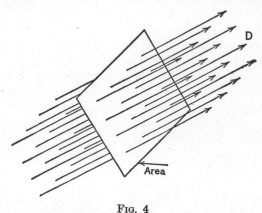

Fig. 4

A general expression which covers all cases, and so may be taken as the definition of **flux,** is as follows:

$$\text{Electrostatic flux} = \int \kappa \mathbf{E} \cdot d\mathbf{a} \qquad [8]$$

The notation of this expression is explained in the next chapter, but its meaning is clear from the above discussion.

Since equation 8 can be written

$$\text{Electrostatic flux} = \int \mathbf{D} \cdot d\mathbf{a} \qquad [9]$$

it follows that the vector quantity $\mathbf{D}$, first used in equation 7, is **electrostatic flux density.**

It is now apparent that the left-hand member of equation 6 or 7 is flux passing through a closed surface. The equation, then, is a mathematical formulation of the following statement: the flux passing through a closed surface is proportional to the electric charge contained within the surface. If each flux line represents a unit amount of flux there will be 4π lines issuing from each unit of positive charge, and 4π lines terminating on each unit of negative charge. In space where there is no electric charge the flux lines must be continuous, for they cannot terminate.

Lines of flux from a charge $+Q$ to a charge $-Q$, are shown in Fig. 5.

If the dash line a is taken to indicate a closed surface about $+Q$, it is evident that all flux lines issuing from the charge must penetrate the surface a. By counting the flux lines that pass through the surface, therefore, it is possible to know how much charge is within the surface. All lines crossing the surface c are going inward; hence there is negative charge within c. Over surfaces b and d the algebraic sum of flux lines is zero.

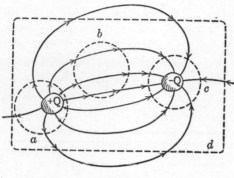

FIG. 5

The choice of a value for h is important, for it determines the size of the unit of electric charge (by relating it to $\mathbf{E}$, which is defined in terms of force). Different values have been given to h in defining different systems of electrical units, but in the Gaussian and electrostatic systems it is given the value 4π. This provides that in free space there will be unit electric field strength 1 centimeter from a unit point charge, a relation that follows from the fact that the area of a sphere of unit radius is 4π (see Problem 1).

A large amount of information about electrostatic fields can be deduced from equations 2, 3, and 9. This is done by mathematical methods, and the most convenient mathematics to use is vector analysis. It is desirable, therefore, to precede further study of the electric field by introducing some of the general mathematical relations of vector analysis.

PROBLEMS

1. Electric field strength is measured at all points of a spherical surface of unit radius, in free space. It is found to be everywhere normal to the surface, one unit in magnitude, and directed outward. How much electric charge is contained within the spherical surface? (Assume the value of h in equation 4 to be 4π.)

2. In the electrostatic system of units a force of 1 dyne is exerted on unit charge (1 statcoulomb) in an electric field of unit intensity (1 statvolt per centimeter). What field intensity, expressed in volts per centimeter, would exert a force of 1 ounce on the same charge?

Chapter II

VECTOR ANALYSIS

VECTOR MULTIPLICATION. Vectors are useful for various purposes. Force can be represented by a vector. So can distance. If a force **F** acts on a body while that body is moving through a distance **s**, as in Fig. 6a, the work done by the force is the product of force and distance. But it is not the simple algebraic product, for the angle between the

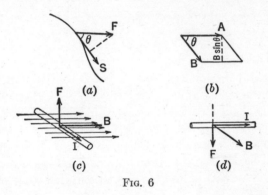

FIG. 6

direction of the force and the direction of travel is important. If the magnitude of the force is represented by F and the magnitude of the distance by s, and the angle between their directions is θ, then the work done is

$$W = Fs \cos \theta \qquad [10]$$

Note that the vector quantities for force and distance are written **F** and **s**, whereas their scalar magnitudes are F and s; this system of notation is rather generally adopted and will be used consistently in the present discussion.

Since the type of multiplication indicated in equation 10 is quite common in physical problems it is given a special symbol in vector analysis: when two vectors are written with a dot between them it is an indication of multiplication of this type. Hence equation 10 may be written

$$W = \mathbf{F} \cdot \mathbf{s} \qquad [11]$$

In the general case of any two vectors **A** and **B** the so-called "scalar product" or "dot product" is defined as follows:

$$\mathbf{A} \cdot \mathbf{B} = AB \cos \theta \qquad [12]$$

As in the case of work, in equation 11, this kind of product is always a scalar quantity, although the quantities multiplied together are both vectors. It is for this reason that it is called the **scalar product**.

There is also another type of multiplication commonly encountered in physical problems. The simplest example is the computation of area, as in Fig. 6b, where two vectors **A** and **B** are shown as the sides of a parallelogram. The area of the parallelogram is

$$\text{Area} = AB \sin \theta \qquad [13]$$

The same type of multiplication is encountered in finding the force on a conductor carrying current in a magnetic field. In Fig. 6c current of I units (amperes in the practical system, statamperes in the Gaussian, a *scalar* quantity) is flowing in a conductor the direction and length of which are represented by a *vector* **L**. The magnetic field is represented in magnitude and direction by the vector **B**. Then the force on the conductor will be the vector quantity **F** which is perpendicular to both **L** and **B**. This defines its direction, and its magnitude is given by

$$F = \frac{I}{c} LB \sin \theta \qquad [14]$$

The value of c, a constant of proportionality, depends on the system of units. The sense of the force is upward in the figure, in accordance with the rule for force in a magnetic field.

Because this type of multiplication is quite common, it also is given a special symbol. The vectors **L** and **B** are written with a cross between them so that equation 14 is written

$$\mathbf{F} = \frac{I}{c} \mathbf{L} \times \mathbf{B} \qquad [15]$$

This type of operation gives what is known as the **cross product** or **vector product**. The latter name comes from the fact that the result of this type of multiplication, such as the force in equation 15, is itself a vector.

It is not at once apparent that the area of Fig. 6b is a vector quantity. But a surface obviously does have an orientation in space, and, by convention, an area is represented by a vector whose direction is *normal* to the surface, and with length proportional to the area. Hence the area of Fig. 6b is represented by a vector perpendicular to the plane of the paper.

A question naturally arises regarding the sense of the resultant vector, such as **F** in equation 15. What is there in the equation to signify whether the force is upward or downward? If, for example, **L** and **B** were to be interchanged, as indicated in Fig. 6d, the magnitude of the force would be unchanged but the sense would be reversed and would become downward. To avoid ambiguity in the mathematical statement of such a problem the vector product is so defined that the sense of the resultant vector is indicated by the order in which the two component vectors are written.

This is a useful and thoroughly satisfactory means of defining the direction of the vector product. Yet expressing in words the defining relation is somewhat awkward. It is customary to remember the relation by a certain arrangement of fingers and thumb on the right hand, or in terms of the rotation of a so-called "right-hand" screw thread.

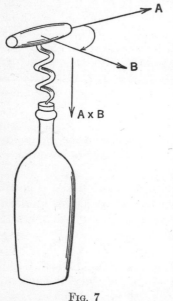

Fig. 7

The product of two vectors, **A**×**B**, is itself a vector of magnitude $AB \sin \theta$, in direction normal to the plane that contains both **A** and **B**, and of such sense that if a right-hand screw (see Fig. 7) were rotated from **A** to **B** (through the angle that is less than 180 degrees) it would screw in the direction of the product.

Following this rule, equation 15 is seen to give the proper direction of force in either Fig. 6c or 6d, and the vector **A**×**B** which represents area in Fig. 6b is properly *into* the sheet of paper. Note, however, that the product **B**×**A** is, by the same rule, a vector directed *outward* from the sheet of paper; this is merely an illustration of the general rule that

$$\mathbf{B} \times \mathbf{A} = -(\mathbf{A} \times \mathbf{B}) \qquad [16]$$

It will be seen that this operation does not follow the fundamental commutative law of ordinary algebra which says that $ab = ba$. It is natural to question what justification there can be for denying a fundamental law of algebra, and a short discussion may be helpful in this connection.

All the operations of algebra, including multiplication, are defined for use with numbers. The rule for multiplication is particularly easy for integers; for instance, 7 times 5 is five 7's added together (or, by the commutative law, it is also the sum of seven 5's). This rule is extended quite readily to the multiplication of fractions, and by an additional convention regarding sign it can be made to serve for negative numbers also. But it simply has no meaning if one tries to apply it to vectors. There are, however, certain operations so commonly performed upon vectors that it seems desirable to give them names; two of these operations are discussed above, and the confusing thing about the situation is that they are *both* called multiplication. Actually, it is very doubtful if either should properly be called multiplication; probably that name should be reserved for the algebraic product of two *scalar* quantities, and completely new names could then be assigned to the operations upon vectors that are known (however improperly) as vector multiplication leading to the scalar product, in one case, and the vector product, in the other. But the nomenclature is so well established that it cannot be avoided.[1]

It now becomes clear that since the vector product is not algebraic multiplication, but is defined quite independently, it is not constrained to follow algebraic laws. It is not surprising that the commutative law fails to apply to the vector product. Rather, it is to be remarked that the commutative law does apply in the case of the scalar product, as defined in equation 12.

UNIT VECTORS. No single expression has yet been given to define the vector product. The following may be used, although it requires a short explanation:

$$\mathbf{A} \times \mathbf{B} = \mathbf{n} \, AB \sin \theta \qquad [17]$$

In this expression, A and B are the scalar magnitudes of $\mathbf{A}$ and $\mathbf{B}$, θ is the angle between $\mathbf{A}$ and $\mathbf{B}$, and $\mathbf{n}$ is a vector of unit length in a direction normal to both $\mathbf{A}$ and $\mathbf{B}$ and with sense, as defined above, forming a right-hand system with $\mathbf{A}$ and $\mathbf{B}$.

The right-hand side of equation 17 illustrates a method of describing a vector. The magnitude of the vector product is given by $AB \sin \theta$,

---

[1] Yet another kind of multiplication, so called, is defined for use with complex quantities. This is the operation according to which

$$(Ae^{j\alpha})(Be^{j\beta}) = ABe^{j(\alpha+\beta)}$$

This law is familiar to students of alternating-current phenomena, for it is very widely used in connection with a convention that makes it possible to represent real quantities that vary sinusoidally with time by means of complex quantities. The complex quantities, which are themselves scalar, can then be represented by rotating vectors in the complex plane. This may be considered a third type of multiplication of vectors, entirely different from either of the other two.

but this expression does not give direction. The unit vector **n** serves to define a direction normal to **A** and **B**, and thereby specifies the direction of the vector product. This artifice of employing a unit vector[2] to give direction is very often useful.

The most common use of unit vectors to define direction is in con-

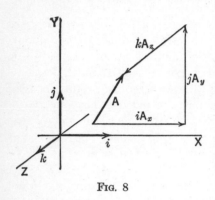

FIG. 8

nection with coordinate axes. In Fig. 8 three axes are shown, marked X, Y, and Z. The position of any point in space may be defined by reference to such axes, in the familiar manner of analytic geometry, using Cartesian coordinates. Similarly, the length and direction of any vector can be expressed by giving the projections of the vector upon the three axes. Any vector **A** may be described as being made up of three mutually perpendicular

components (as in Fig. 8): A_x in the x direction, A_y in the y direction, A_z in the z direction.

Now A_x is a scalar quantity. It is the *length* of the x component of **A**. A_y and A_z are also scalar quantities. It is consequently not correct to say that the vector **A** is equal to the sum of A_x, A_y, and A_z. But it is correct to say that **A** is equal to the sum of a vector in the x direction of length A_x, a vector in the y direction of length A_y, and a vector in the z direction of length A_z.

Such a statement of equality is cumbersome, but it can be simplified by defining three unit vectors as follows: The vector **i** is a vector of unit length in the x direction (see Fig. 8); the vector **j** is a vector of unit length in the y direction; the vector **k** is a vector of unit length in the z direction. Now when it becomes necessary to write of " a vector in the x direction of length A_x " it is only necessary to set down " iA_x," which expresses exactly the same idea. So it is correct to write

$$\mathbf{A} = \mathbf{i}A_x + \mathbf{j}A_y + \mathbf{k}A_z \qquad [18]$$

and this notation will be used frequently.

Products involving these unit vectors are of frequent occurrence and

[2] It should be noted that no equation can be correct unless either both sides are scalar quantities or both sides are vector quantities. A vector cannot be equated to a scalar. Hence equation 17 could not be correct in the absence of the symbol **n**, for without it the left-hand member would be a vector and the right-hand member a scalar.

deserve special consideration. Consider the dot product $\mathbf{i} \cdot \mathbf{i}$; both
$\mathbf{i}$'s are of unit length and the angle between them is zero; therefore, by
equation 12, the product is unity, a scalar value. But consider $\mathbf{i} \cdot \mathbf{j}$;
the angle between these two is 90 degrees; hence by equation 12 their
product is zero. Physically, the projection of $\mathbf{i}$ upon $\mathbf{i}$ is unity, and
the projection of $\mathbf{i}$ upon $\mathbf{j}$ is zero.

Consider the vector product $\mathbf{i} \times \mathbf{j}$; by equation 17 the product will be
a vector of unit length normal to both $\mathbf{i}$ and $\mathbf{j}$, and in the direction that
would be taken by a right-hand screw while being rotated from $\mathbf{i}$ to $\mathbf{j}$.
A moment's study of Fig. 8 shows that this product is identical with $\mathbf{k}$.
Hence $\mathbf{i} \times \mathbf{j} = \mathbf{k}$. But note that $\mathbf{j} \times \mathbf{i} = -\mathbf{k}$.

Because the angle between two similar unit vectors is zero, it is
apparent from equation 17 that $\mathbf{i} \times \mathbf{i}$ is zero. This is illustrated by the
fact that the area of a parallelogram, as in Fig. 6b, approaches zero as
the two adjacent sides approach each other.

A partial tabulation of products of unit vectors follows:

$$\mathbf{i} \cdot \mathbf{i} = 1 \qquad \mathbf{i} \times \mathbf{i} = 0$$

$$\mathbf{i} \cdot \mathbf{j} = 0 \qquad \mathbf{i} \times \mathbf{j} = \mathbf{k} \qquad [19]$$

$$\mathbf{i} \cdot \mathbf{k} = 0 \qquad \mathbf{i} \times \mathbf{k} = -\mathbf{j}$$

Coordinate systems are essential in connection with vector analysis,
and it will be helpful to express some of the more important vector
operations in terms of Cartesian components. (A right-hand system
of rectangular coordinates, as in Fig. 8, is used.)

The scalar product of any two vectors $\mathbf{A}$ and $\mathbf{B}$ may be expanded into

$$\mathbf{A} \cdot \mathbf{B} = A_x B_x + A_y B_y + A_z B_z \qquad [20]$$

To prove that this is true, substitute equation 18 for $\mathbf{A}$ and a similar
expression for $\mathbf{B}$, and multiply term by term:

$$\mathbf{A} \cdot \mathbf{B} = (\mathbf{i} A_x + \mathbf{j} A_y + \mathbf{k} A_z) \cdot (\mathbf{i} B_x + \mathbf{j} B_y + \mathbf{k} B_z)$$

$$= \mathbf{i} \cdot \mathbf{i} A_x B_x + \mathbf{j} \cdot \mathbf{j} A_y B_y + \mathbf{k} \cdot \mathbf{k} A_z B_z$$

$$+ \mathbf{i} \cdot \mathbf{j} A_x B_y + \mathbf{i} \cdot \mathbf{k} A_x B_z + \mathbf{j} \cdot \mathbf{i} A_y B_x + \mathbf{j} \cdot \mathbf{k} A_y B_z$$

$$+ \mathbf{k} \cdot \mathbf{i} A_z B_x + \mathbf{k} \cdot \mathbf{j} A_z B_y \qquad [21]$$

The first three terms of this expansion give the right-hand member of
equation 20, for the dot products of identical vectors are unity, and the
other six terms disappear because all the dot products of the unlike
vectors are zero.

As a physical illustration of the expansion of the scalar product in
equation 20, consider the product of the force $\mathbf{F}$ and the distance $\mathbf{s}$ as

shown in Fig. 9. The coordinate axes are selected in such a way that both force and distance lie in the X-Y plane, so the problem is merely a two-dimensional one. The vectors shown have the components F_x and F_y, and S_x and S_y. It is physically evident that the component of force F_x acting through the distance S_y does not represent any work, for the force and distance are perpendicular. The same is true for the force F_y acting through the distance S_x. But the force F_x applied through the distance S_x results in work equal to $F_x S_x$, and the other components give $F_y S_y$. These latter terms, consequently, are retained in the scalar product, the full three-dimensional form of which is given in equation 20, while products of components along different axes (the zero terms of equation 21) contribute nothing to the scalar product.

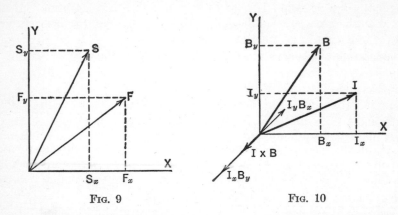

FIG. 9   FIG. 10

The vector product, or cross product, of any two vectors may be expanded in a similar manner:

$$\mathbf{A} \times \mathbf{B} = \mathbf{i}(A_y B_z - A_z B_y) + \mathbf{j}(A_z B_x - A_x B_z) + \mathbf{k}(A_x B_y - A_y B_x) \quad [22]$$

The proof of this is exactly parallel to the proof of equation 20.

A physical illustration of the significance of terms in equation 22 is found in considering a current $\mathbf{I}$ and a magnetic field $\mathbf{B}$, and the force $\frac{1}{c} \mathbf{I} \times \mathbf{B}$ that results upon the current-carrying conductor. Select coordinates so that $\mathbf{I}$ and $\mathbf{B}$ both lie in the X-Y plane, as in Fig. 10. The current component I_x and the magnetic field component B_x do not react, for there is no force on a current parallel to a magnetic field. But I_x and B_y, being at right angles, react to give the force $\frac{1}{c} I_x B_y$ in the direction of the Z axis. And I_y and B_x produce a force of magnitude $\frac{1}{c} I_y B_x$

that is directed along the Z axis in the negative direction.   **Total force** consequently is the algebraic sum of these two, or

$$\frac{1}{c} \left(I_x B_y - I_y B_x \right)$$

This expression will be seen to correspond to the last term of equation 22.   The other terms of equation 22 appear if I and B have Z components also.   Products of components with like subscripts, such as $I_x B_x$, or $I_y B_y$, do not appear in the expansion of the vector product.

It is convenient to express the expansion of the vector product as a determinant, and it makes it easier to remember.

$$\mathbf{A} \times \mathbf{B} = \begin{vmatrix} \mathbf{i} & \mathbf{j} & \mathbf{k} \\ A_x & A_y & A_z \\ B_x & B_y & B_z \end{vmatrix} \tag{23}$$

If this determinant is expanded according to the ordinary rules (which may be found in algebra books, or in the mathematical sections of handbooks) it is identical with equation 22.

TRIPLE PRODUCTS.   The vector product of two vectors is itself a vector, and its product with some other vector may be found.   The second multiplication may be either a scalar or a vector product, thus:

$$(\mathbf{A} \times \mathbf{B}) \cdot \mathbf{C} \tag{24}$$

or

$$(\mathbf{A} \times \mathbf{B}) \times \mathbf{C} \tag{25}$$

These are obviously different, and must be considered one at a time.

First consider expression 24. If $\mathbf{A}$, $\mathbf{B}$, and $\mathbf{C}$ are any three vectors, as in Fig. 11, the scalar triple product of expression 24 is the volume of the parallelopiped shown, of which $\mathbf{A}$, $\mathbf{B}$, and $\mathbf{C}$ are the three edges. This is evident when it is realized that $\mathbf{A} \times \mathbf{B}$ is the area of the top of the parallelopiped, and $(\mathbf{A} \times \mathbf{B}) \cdot \mathbf{C}$ is the product of this area and the normal component of the edge $\mathbf{C}$.

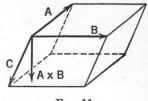

FIG. 11

The volume of the same parallelopiped will be found when the area of the side bounded by $\mathbf{B}$ and $\mathbf{C}$ is multiplied by the normal component of $\mathbf{A}$, and consequently

$$(\mathbf{A} \times \mathbf{B}) \cdot \mathbf{C} = (\mathbf{B} \times \mathbf{C}) \cdot \mathbf{A} \tag{26}$$

and similarly either of these is equal to $(\mathbf{C} \times \mathbf{A}) \cdot \mathbf{B}$.

This scalar triple product is sometimes written [ABC] and this is an adequate notation, for a little study will show that the vectors may be multiplied in any order provided the cyclic order **ABC** be retained, but that

$$[ABC] = -[CBA] \tag{27}$$

The dot and cross may be inserted as desired in expression 27.

The vector triple product, expression 25, leads to a vector that lies in the same plane as **A** and **B**. It may be expanded as follows:

$$(A{\times}B){\times}C = B(C \cdot A) - A(B \cdot C) \tag{28}$$

Proof of this expansion will not be given, but it is quite simply obtained by expansion of both sides of equation 28 in rectangular coordinates.

VECTOR FIELDS. Vector and scalar fields may be plotted or diagrammed in various ways, and plotting such fields is helpful in understanding their mathematical behavior.

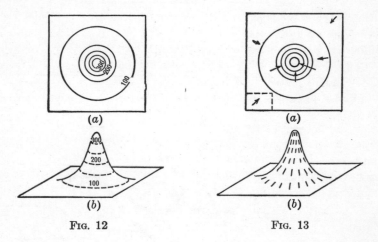

FIG. 12   FIG. 13

Contour maps are particularly interesting because they are plots of a scalar field, elevation. Figure 12, for instance, is a map of a mountain. It is a singularly symmetrical mountain, rising to a peak in the center of the map. Elevation, as plotted on a contour map, is a scalar quantity: each point is at an elevation of so many feet, and when all points of equal elevation are connected by contour lines the form of the earth's surface is completely defined.

Consider a marble placed upon the mountain of Fig. 12; it will try to roll down hill. Wherever it is placed upon the mountain slope, a certain force will be required to hold it, and in this way a vector field of force is defined. In Fig. 13a, another map of the mountain, arrows are drawn to indicate the amount and direction of the force required to hold the marble at various places. Such arrows are not essentially different from the *hachure* markings commonly used on geographic maps to indicate mountains, as shown in Fig. 13b. A map with hachure marks may be considered to be a rather primitive plot of a vector field.

It is apparent that there is a relation between the scalar field of elevation and the vector field of force-on-a-marble. It is a simple and familiar one: The force is dependent upon the steepness of the slope, or in other words, upon the rate of change of elevation with respect to distance.

This rate of change is a derivative, similar in nature to the ordinary derivative of differential calculus. It is complicated, however, by the necessity of finding the direction of steepest slope to determine the *direction* in which the marble will tend to roll. The steepest slope at a given point is known as the **gradient** at that point. It is a vector quantity at each point, and therefore constitutes a vector field.

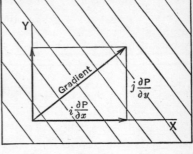

Fig. 14

GRADIENT. In the lower-left corner of Fig. 13a a section of the map is indicated by dash lines. This rectangular section is enlarged in Fig. 14, and a pair of coordinate axes is superimposed for reference purposes. The gradient in this small section of the field is practically uniform, being much the same at all points in magnitude and direction, and it is indicated by a vector. This vector of gradient is made up of two components, one the steepness in the x direction, $\dfrac{\partial P}{\partial x}$, and the other the steepness in the y direction, $\dfrac{\partial P}{\partial y}$. Elevation is indicated by the symbol[3] P, and in this two-dimensional field

$$\text{Gradient} = \mathbf{i}\,\frac{\partial P}{\partial x} + \mathbf{j}\,\frac{\partial P}{\partial y} \qquad [29]$$

Two characteristics of gradient are so important that they must be mentioned at once. First, the gradient vector will always be at right angles to the contour lines. This is evident because the gradient is the steepest slope; the steepest slope will be found in descending unit elevation in the shortest horizontal distance; travel from one contour line

[3] The symbol P is used because elevation is a gravitational *potential*.

to the next results in unit change of elevation and this is accomplished in the shortest horizontal distance by taking a path perpendicular to the contour lines.

Second, the closer the contour lines are spaced, the steeper the slope and the greater the gradient.

If the elevation at every point is known, and can be expressed analytically, giving P in terms of x and y, it is easy to apply equation 29. A simple example may be considered, referring to Fig. 14: Elevation at the origin is 1000 feet, and the hillside slopes up to the northeast. When traveling due east the ground rises 4 feet per mile, while toward the north the slope is 3 feet per mile, and so (within this limited region) elevation at any point can be found from

$$P = 1000 + 4x + 3y \qquad [30]$$

Substituting equation 30 into equation 29 gives

$$\text{Gradient} = \mathbf{i}\,4 + \mathbf{j}\,3 \qquad [31]$$

This indicates that the slope is everywhere the same (x and y do not appear in equation 31), and in such a direction that a rolling marble would go 3 feet south for each 4 feet west. The steepest slope, or gradient, is equal to the square root of the sum of the squares of the component slopes and is 5 feet per mile.

Another numerical example will illustrate a slightly less simple case: Consider the origin of coordinates to be at the top of a 1000-foot hill of such a shape that

$$P = 1000 - x^2 - y^2 \qquad [32]$$

Equation 29 gives

$$\text{Gradient} = -\mathbf{i}\,2x - \mathbf{j}\,2y \qquad [33]$$

The gradient is zero when x and y are zero, which is natural, for that is the precise top of the hill. As one moves out in any direction the gradient becomes greater. The gradient, moreover, differs in direction at different points of the hill's surface. Full information is given by equation 33.

The above discussion of gradient refers to a two-dimensional field or surface. An electric field is a three-dimensional field in space. Flow of water as, for example, circulating currents in a large tank may be represented by a three-dimensional vector field wherein the vectors represent velocity of flow. Temperature in a large block of unequally heated metal is a three-dimensional scalar field. Flow of heat in such a block of metal is determined by the temperature gradient.

A three-dimensional gradient, such as this gradient of temperature, is exactly analogous to the two-dimensional gradient of elevation that has been considered, and its definition is similar. Given a three-dimensional scalar field P, the gradient of P is the vector field given by

$$\text{Gradient of } P = \mathbf{i}\frac{\partial P}{\partial x} + \mathbf{j}\frac{\partial P}{\partial y} + \mathbf{k}\frac{\partial P}{\partial z} \qquad [34]$$

Equation 29, in which P is a function of x and y only, is a special case of this more general definition.

DIVERGENCE. The quantity called gradient is a rate of change in a scalar field. A vector field also changes from point to point, but in a more complicated manner. It cannot be said to have a gradient, but there are other ways in which the rate of change of a vector field can be described. One of the most useful is known as **divergence**. The divergence of a vector field **A** is:

$$\text{Divergence of } \mathbf{A} = \frac{\partial A_x}{\partial x} + \frac{\partial A_y}{\partial y} + \frac{\partial A_z}{\partial z} \qquad [35]$$

A_x is the magnitude of the x component of **A**, and since **A** is a three-dimensional vector field, A_x is a three-dimensional scalar field. A_x may vary from point to point and is, in general, a function of x, y, and z. Its derivative with respect to x is the first term of equation 35. The second and third terms are found in similar manner from the y and z components of **A**.

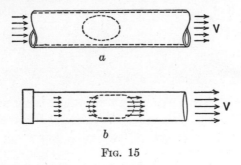

FIG. 15

It has been mentioned that divergence is a useful quantity. Its application is nicely illustrated in the flow of fluids. Figure 15a shows a pipe through which water is flowing. The dash line within the pipe represents an imaginary surface; water passes through this surface. The surface is completely closed, and water will flow in through one side and out through the other. The water may flow in any irregular fashion whatever, but (since water is incompressible) the same amount of water must flow out that flows in. It will be proved a little later that this is the same as saying that water, being incompressible, must flow in such a way that if its velocity is represented by the vector field **V**, the divergence of **V** must everywhere be zero.   It is from this concept that the name " divergence " arises: Water cannot diverge from any point for it would leave a vacuum; it cannot converge to any point for it is incompressible.

But the flow of air is different.   Figure 15*b* represents a tube of compressed air, capped on one end.   A similar cap has just been removed from the other end and air is rushing out.   Consider the closed surface within the tube that is represented by a dash line; because the air is expanding, more air is passing out (through one end) of the indicated surface than is entering the surface (through the other end). Consequently there is a divergence of air.   There is divergence at every point where air is expanding and, if velocity of air is the vector field **V**, the divergence of **V** is not zero.

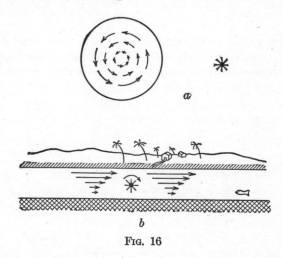

a

b

FIG. 16

CURL.   Another important way of describing a rate of change in a vector field is given the name of **curl**.   Consider a tub of water; Fig. 16*a* shows the tub as seen from above.   The water in it has been stirred with a paddle and the vectors represent velocity, **V**.   A small paddle-wheel is shown beside the tub; if this paddle-wheel, mounted on frictionless bearings, is dipped into the center of the tub it will be turned in a counterclockwise direction.   At whatever point the paddle-wheel may be placed in the tub it will be turned by the water, for even if it is not in the center of the tub the water will be going more rapidly past one side of the wheel than past the other.   The turning of the paddle-wheel is an indication that the water is moving in the tub in such a way that the vector field of velocity has a rate of change of the type called " curl."

The name " curl " indicates an association with motion in curved lines. This is not necessary, however, for straight-line motion may also have curl. If water flows in a canal, as in Fig. 16b, in such a way that it flows more rapidly near the surface than it does along the bottom of the canal, every particle of water may move in a straight line but nevertheless there is curl, as will be recognized when an exploring paddle-wheel is considered. The exploring wheel as seen in the figure will be turned in a clockwise direction, for the stream is more rapid on its upper blades than on its lower ones.

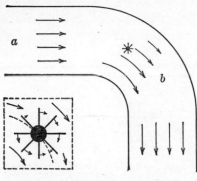

FIG. 17

Figure 17 shows a map of another canal, in which the water flows without curl. In the straight part of the canal the velocity of flow is uniform, and it is obvious that the paddle-wheel at position a will not turn. At b, in a bend of the canal, it is possible for water to turn the corner without curl, provided it flows faster along the inner margin of the channel in just the right proportion. An enlarged view of the paddle-wheel at b is shown (it must be understood that the exploring paddle-wheel is in fact so small that it does not interfere with the flow of water), and little arrows indicate the reaction of the water on each of its blades. Because of the curvature of the lines of flow, more than half of the blades are driven clockwise. But the velocity of water is greater on the inner side, and although fewer blades are driven counter-clockwise they are each acted on more forcefully. It is readily conceivable that curvature and variation of velocity might be so related that the wheel would have no total tendency to turn. Curved motion is therefore possible without curl. This kind of flow is, as a matter of fact, characteristic of a truly frictionless liquid. It is the purpose of " streamlining " to provide a surface past which air or water will flow with a minimum of curl, for motion with curl develops eddies that waste energy.

Divergence of a vector field is a *scalar* quantity. There is divergence from a point or to a point (positive or negative), but no idea of direction is involved. Curl of a vector field, on the contrary, is a *vector*. If curl is visualized as an eddy, it is evident that the eddy must be about some axis — perhaps a vertical axis, perhaps horizontal, perhaps at some angle. The direction of such an axis is, by definition, the direction of the vector that represents curl. Referring to the hypothetical paddle-wheel, when it is in the position in which it turns most rapidly, its axis is in the direction of the curl vector. Each component of the vector of curl may be found by placing the paddle-wheel axis parallel to the appropriate axis of coordinates.

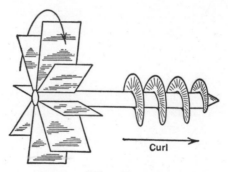

Curl

Fig. 18

The sense of the curl vector is determined by the direction of rotation of the paddle-wheel: if the paddle-wheel turns a right-hand screw it will screw itself in the direction of the curl vector, as in Fig. 18.

Mathematically the curl of a vector field **A** is defined by

$$\text{Curl of } \mathbf{A} = \mathbf{i}\left(\frac{\partial A_z}{\partial y} - \frac{\partial A_y}{\partial z}\right) + \mathbf{j}\left(\frac{\partial A_x}{\partial z} - \frac{\partial A_z}{\partial x}\right) + \mathbf{k}\left(\frac{\partial A_y}{\partial x} - \frac{\partial A_x}{\partial y}\right) \quad [36]$$

It will be shown later that this is equivalent to the physical concept of curl that has been discussed in the preceding paragraphs.

NABLA. Time is saved in writing the equations of vector analysis, and, what is more important, they are made easier to remember, by the use of a symbol known as " nabla " and written ∇.[4] Its formal defi-

---

[4] This symbol is frequently given the name " del," but this has been found to lead to confusion with the Greek letter " delta " which is similar in appearance but which conveys an entirely different mathematical meaning. Therefore the Hamiltonian name of " nabla " is returning to common use and is recommended, for example, by the American Institute of Electrical Engineers. The original nabla was a Hebrew harp of triangular shape, נ ב ל, the psaltery of the Psalms.

nition is

$$\nabla \equiv \mathbf{i}\frac{\partial}{\partial x} + \mathbf{j}\frac{\partial}{\partial y} + \mathbf{k}\frac{\partial}{\partial z} \qquad [37]$$

It will be seen that this symbol by itself has no meaning. It has the formal appearance of a vector for which the x, y, and z components are respectively $\dfrac{\partial}{\partial x}$, $\dfrac{\partial}{\partial y}$, and $\dfrac{\partial}{\partial z}$. But, like $\dfrac{\partial}{\partial x}$, *nabla* is an *operator*, and must have something on which to operate. If it is allowed to operate on a scalar function it gives the gradient of that function; operating on P it gives

$$\nabla P = \mathbf{i}\frac{\partial}{\partial x}P + \mathbf{j}\frac{\partial}{\partial y}P + \mathbf{k}\frac{\partial}{\partial z}P \qquad [38]$$

and this, by comparison with equation 34, is seen to be the gradient of P. The expression ∇P is expanded exactly as if it were the product of a vector quantity ∇ by a scalar quantity P. Actually it is not a multiplication at all, but an operation of differentiation.

The symbol ∇, as defined in equation 37, can be put through many algebraic transformations as if it were indeed a vector quantity, and this is one of the advantages of its use. For instance, a quantity written formally as the dot product of ∇ and a vector field gives the divergence of that field. Referring to equation 20 we write:

$$\nabla \cdot \mathbf{B} = \frac{\partial}{\partial x}B_x + \frac{\partial}{\partial y}B_y + \frac{\partial}{\partial z}B_z \qquad [39]$$

which, by comparison with equation 35, is the divergence of $\mathbf{B}$.

Similarly, a quantity written as the cross product of ∇ and a vector field gives the curl of that field. Referring to equation 22 the cross product is expanded:

$$\nabla^\times \mathbf{B} = \mathbf{i}\left(\frac{\partial}{\partial y}B_z - \frac{\partial}{\partial z}B_y\right) + \mathbf{j}\left(\frac{\partial}{\partial z}B_x - \frac{\partial}{\partial x}B_z\right) + \mathbf{k}\left(\frac{\partial}{\partial x}B_y - \frac{\partial}{\partial y}B_x\right) \qquad [40]$$

and by comparison with equation 36 this is recognized as the curl of $\mathbf{B}$.

The equation for curl is formally similar to the equation for the cross product, and it also may be expressed as a determinant. The determinantal form is much easier to remember than the expanded form of equation 40: it is

$$\nabla^\times \mathbf{B} = \begin{vmatrix} \mathbf{i} & \mathbf{j} & \mathbf{k} \\ \dfrac{\partial}{\partial x} & \dfrac{\partial}{\partial y} & \dfrac{\partial}{\partial z} \\ B_x & B_y & B_z \end{vmatrix} \qquad [41]$$

The following tabulation collects information relating to differential operations on vector and scalar fields.

Type of operation	Symbol	Must be applied to a:	Yields a:
Gradient of A	∇A	Scalar field	Vector field
Divergence of **A**	$\nabla \cdot \mathbf{A}$	Vector field	Scalar field
Curl of **A**	$\nabla \times \mathbf{A}$	Vector field	Vector field

Illustrative Examples. The most satisfactory way to become familiar with gradient, divergence, and curl is by study of a few simple illustrations of vector fields. These will be mere geometrical fields, with no physical meaning attached at the present time. Some of them will later be found to be of electromagnetic importance.

Only two-dimensional fields will be considered in this section; an extension to three dimensions is simple when the two-dimensional case is understood, and two-dimensional illustrations are clearer because of being less obscured by mathematical manipulation. Moreover, a great many practical cases in three dimensions can be reduced to two-variable problems by such choice of coordinate axes that the quantities being studied are functions of two variables only.

When working with a scalar field that is the same for all values of z, and therefore has derivatives with respect to x and y only, it is evident from equation 38 that the gradient is merely

$$\nabla P = \mathbf{i}\frac{\partial P}{\partial x} + \mathbf{j}\frac{\partial P}{\partial y} \qquad [42]$$

For a two-variable vector field **A**, divergence is

$$\nabla \cdot \mathbf{A} = \frac{\partial A_x}{\partial x} + \frac{\partial A_y}{\partial y} \qquad [43]$$

If it is also true that the vector field has no component in the z direction ($A_z = 0$) the curl is

$$\nabla \times \mathbf{A} = \mathbf{k}\left(\frac{\partial A_y}{\partial x} - \frac{\partial A_x}{\partial y}\right) \qquad [44]$$

Equations of vector analysis are collected for ready reference in Table II (inside back cover).

Example 1. Consider a vector field defined by the equations

$$A_x = 1 \quad A_y = 2$$

These are, of course, the components of the vector field **A** and

$$\mathbf{A} = \mathbf{i}A_x + \mathbf{j}A_y = \mathbf{i}1 + \mathbf{j}2$$

In Fig. 19a this field is indicated, the lines showing the direction of the vectors; it has already been mentioned that graphical representation of a vector field is not easy and some effort of visualization will be required. From the defining equation it is seen that the field intensity at any point (P in the figure) is 1 unit in the x direction and 2 units in the y direction, as shown. This is the same everywhere, for neither A_x nor A_y is a function of either x or y. This field has neither divergence nor curl. That there is no divergence is shown when A_x and A_y are substituted into equation 43, for the partial derivatives are both zero. Likewise there is no curl, for the partial derivatives of equation 44 are both zero.

Example 2. Consider a vector field defined by

$$A_x = y + 10 \quad A_y = 0$$

This field is shown in Fig. 19b. The field is entirely in the x direction because A_y is everywhere zero, and it becomes more intense toward the top because A_x increases with y; this is shown in the figure by drawing the lines that indicate direction of the field closer together in the more intense region (as is customarily done with magnetic and electric lines of force). If y were less than -10 the direction of the field would reverse, and along the line $y = -10$ there is zero field, but the diagram is not extended to that region.

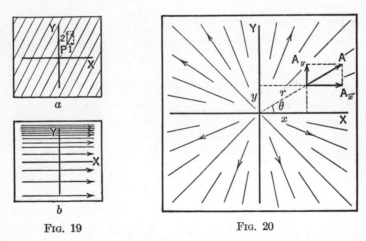

FIG. 19   FIG. 20

Equation 43 tells us that this field has no divergence. In applying equation 44 we find that $\partial A_y / \partial x = 0$, but $\partial A_x / \partial y = 1$. Hence the curl of the field is everywhere $-\mathbf{k}$. (Consider the exploring paddle-wheel or curl-meter of Fig. 18.)

Example 3. Next it is desired to consider a field that has everywhere unit intensity and is everywhere radial from the origin of coordinates in direction. Such a field is suggested in Fig. 20, in which an attempt has been made to keep the density of radial lines everywhere the same. Consider any point, p, with coordinates x and y; since $\mathbf{A}$ is to be radial, A_x must be $A \cos \theta$ and A_y must be $A \sin \theta$. Hence if A is everywhere unity,

$$A_x = \frac{x}{\sqrt{x^2 + y^2}} \quad A_y = \frac{y}{\sqrt{x^2 + y^2}}$$

These equations define the field at all points in any quadrant. In computing divergence and curl it is necessary to determine the four partial derivatives:

$$\frac{\partial A_x}{\partial x} = \frac{1}{(x^2 + y^2)^{1/2}} - \frac{x^2}{(x^2 + y^2)^{3/2}}$$

$$\frac{\partial A_y}{\partial y} = \frac{1}{(x^2 + y^2)^{1/2}} - \frac{y^2}{(x^2 + y^2)^{3/2}}$$

$$\frac{\partial A_y}{\partial x} = - \frac{xy}{(x^2 + y^2)^{3/2}}$$

$$\frac{\partial A_x}{\partial y} = - \frac{xy}{(x^2 + y^2)^{3/2}}$$

Adding the first two to obtain divergence gives

$$\nabla \cdot \mathbf{A} = \frac{1}{(x^2 + y^2)^{1/2}} = \frac{1}{r} \qquad [45]$$

Subtracting the fourth from the third to obtain curl gives

$$\nabla \times \mathbf{A} = 0 \qquad [46]$$

The divergence in this field is particularly interesting. The presence of divergence is associated with the necessity for starting new radial lines in the diagram in order to indicate a constant intensity of field. It is apparent that if lines start within a region of space, there must be more lines coming out of that region than enter it; in such a case there is divergence in that region. Qualitatively, it may be seen in Fig. 20 that divergence is greatest near the origin, for that is where most lines originate; quantitatively, equation 45 tells us that divergence is inversely proportional to radius and increases without limit as the origin is approached.

A differentiating operation upon a field can be repeated, giving a quantity analogous to a second derivative. In the above example the divergence of $\mathbf{A}$ is itself a scalar field of which the gradient can be found.

This will give the gradient of the divergence of **A** (symbolically $\nabla[\nabla \cdot \mathbf{A}]$).

$$\nabla(\nabla \cdot \mathbf{A}) = \nabla \frac{1}{\sqrt{x^2 + y^2}} = \mathbf{i}\frac{\partial}{\partial x}(x^2 + y^2)^{-\frac{1}{2}} + \mathbf{j}\frac{\partial}{\partial y}(x^2 + y^2)^{-\frac{1}{2}}$$

$$= -\mathbf{i}\frac{x}{r^3} - \mathbf{j}\frac{y}{r^3} \qquad [47]$$

This result is a vector field, which we can again differentiate to find its curl or its divergence. Finding its curl, two partial derivatives are needed:

$$\frac{\partial}{\partial x}\left(-\frac{y}{r^3}\right) = \frac{\partial}{\partial x}[-y\,(x^2 + y^2)^{-\frac{3}{2}}] = (-y)(-\tfrac{3}{2})(x^2 - y^2)^{-\frac{5}{2}}\,(2x)$$

$$\frac{\partial}{\partial y}\left(-\frac{x}{r^3}\right) = \frac{\partial}{\partial y}[-x\,(x^2 + y^2)^{-\frac{3}{2}}] = (-x)(-\tfrac{3}{2})(x^2 - y^2)^{-\frac{5}{2}}\,(2y)$$

Subtracting these partial derivatives gives the curl, and since they are equal the curl is zero. That is, the curl of the gradient of $1/r$ is zero:

$$\nabla\times\nabla\frac{1}{r} = 0 \qquad [48]$$

It is not a coincidence, or a special property of this particular field, that the curl of the gradient is zero; it will be shown in the next paragraph that the curl of the gradient of any scalar field is always identically zero.

A FIELD THAT IS THE GRADIENT OF SOMETHING HAS No CURL. ($\nabla\times\nabla F \equiv 0$.) To prove this theorem, consider any scalar field. This field will be denoted by F. First write its gradient, using equation 38:

$$\nabla F = \mathbf{i}\frac{\partial F}{\partial x} + \mathbf{j}\frac{\partial F}{\partial y} + \mathbf{k}\frac{\partial F}{\partial z} \qquad [49]$$

Note that this gradient is a vector with components $\partial F/\partial x$, $\partial F/\partial y$, and $\partial F/\partial z$. The curl of this vector is found by substituting into equation 40:

$$\nabla\times(\nabla F) = \mathbf{i}\left(\frac{\partial}{\partial y}\frac{\partial F}{\partial z} - \frac{\partial}{\partial z}\frac{\partial F}{\partial y}\right) + \mathbf{j}\left(\frac{\partial}{\partial z}\frac{\partial F}{\partial x} - \frac{\partial}{\partial x}\frac{\partial F}{\partial z}\right)$$

$$+ \mathbf{k}\left(\frac{\partial}{\partial x}\frac{\partial F}{\partial y} - \frac{\partial}{\partial y}\frac{\partial F}{\partial x}\right) \qquad [50]$$

This completes the proof, for, since the order of differentiation of a second partial derivative is immaterial, each of the parentheses in the above expression is identically zero.

Another similar theorem states that for any vector field **A**, $\nabla \cdot \nabla\times\mathbf{A} \equiv 0$. In words, *a field that is the curl of something has no* *divergence*. This is illustrated by Problems 12 and 13. The general theorem is easily proved (as Problem 14) by a method quite similar to the proof of the identity $\nabla \times \nabla F \equiv 0$. As in that case, expansion leads to equal and opposite second partial derivatives.

There is one other repeated differentiation of great importance in applications to physical problems, that is, the divergence of the gradient. The divergence of the gradient is of so much importance that it is given a special name; it is called the " Laplacian," after the famous French mathematician of a century and a half ago. It is, moreover, given a special symbol; although the Laplacian of F would properly be written $\nabla \cdot \nabla F$, it has become customary to abbreviate this to $\nabla^2 F$, the meaning of course being the same. The Laplacian, being divergence, is a scalar field. Expressed in terms of second partial derivatives it is extraordinarily simple and of obvious importance:

$$\nabla^2 F = \nabla \cdot (\nabla F) = \nabla \cdot \left(i \frac{\partial F}{\partial x} + j \frac{\partial F}{\partial y} + k \frac{\partial F}{\partial z} \right)$$

$$= \frac{\partial}{\partial x} \frac{\partial F}{\partial x} + \frac{\partial}{\partial y} \frac{\partial F}{\partial y} + \frac{\partial}{\partial z} \frac{\partial F}{\partial z}$$

$$= \left(\frac{\partial^2}{\partial x^2} + \frac{\partial^2}{\partial y^2} + \frac{\partial^2}{\partial z^2} \right) F \qquad [51]$$

The Laplacian is not, in general, equal to zero. (The curl of the gradient and the divergence of the curl are the only two second-derivative operations that are always identically zero.) Yet the Laplacian is frequently zero in physical problems, depending upon the physical conditions. In electrostatics, for instance, the Laplacian of the electric potential is zero in any space that does not contain electric charge; this will be shown in a later chapter.

Equation 51 gives the Laplacian of a scalar field, F. The Laplacian of a vector field is also useful. The Laplacian of the vector field **A** is written $\nabla^2 \mathbf{A}$, and it is interpreted to mean

$$\nabla^2 \mathbf{A} = \nabla^2 (i A_x + j A_y + k A_z) \qquad [52]$$

The Laplacian of a vector field is therefore the vector sum of the Laplacians of the three scalar components of the vector field.[5] It is frequently important to know whether the Laplacian of a vector field is zero. The answer is that it is zero if and only if the Laplacians of the

---

[5] This may be taken as the definition of the Laplacian of a vector field. An alternative definition that gives the Laplacian the same value but avoids defining it in terms of specific coordinates is: $\nabla^2 \mathbf{A} = \nabla(\nabla \cdot \mathbf{A}) - \nabla \times (\nabla \times \mathbf{A})$.

component scalar fields, A_x, A_y, and A_z, are each independently zero.

POLAR COORDINATES. It will have been noticed that several examples and problems in the earlier part of the chapter are naturally adapted to the use of polar coordinates. Example 3 and Fig. 20, for instance, have symmetry about the origin in such a way that reference to the radial distance r and the angle θ could hardly be avoided. Would it not be possible, then, to use polar coordinates instead of rectangular coordinates in connection with fields of radial symmetry, and thereby simplify the calculations?

That question introduces an aspect of vector analysis that is of the utmost importance. It is this. Vector analysis is fundamentally independent of coordinate systems. An electric field, or a field of velocity, or a field of force exists, physically, whether or not any mathematician has yet laid out a set of coordinate axes. The field has divergence or curl or gradient, or it has not, depending upon the properties of the field itself and without regard to any system of coordinates. Scalar products, vector products, sums and differences of vectors, line integrals, and surface integrals are all of significance without reference to coordinates. Nature does not provide systems of coordinates (except in special cases in which the properties of matter are different in different directions).

It is evident that a system of mathematics in which general relations can be stated without reference to coordinates is simpler than a system in which arbitrary axes must first be introduced as a frame upon which to hang the mental processes. Hence the theorems and generalizations of vector analysis are much easier to comprehend than the similar statements of coordinate geometry.

For actual computation, unfortunately, it is usually necessary to refer to coordinates. The axes are required for calculations, for how can a field be defined at every point in space except by identifying each point by means of coordinates? But, at least, generalized thinking can be done in terms of vector analysis, and then any convenient set of coordinates can be used to facilitate computation. It is for this purpose that operations of vector analysis, after being defined in terms of the vectors and the fields themselves (as in equations 12 and 17), are also expressed with reference to a coordinate system (as in equations 20 and 22, and 38, 39, and 40).

Some coordinate systems are more convenient than others in specific computations. As illustrated in Problem 7, the choice of coordinate system makes no difference in the result. And since polar coordinates are better adapted to many problems than are rectangular coordinates, it will be desirable to express some of the vector operations in polar coordinates.

Consider a two-dimensional polar system using as coordinates radial distance r and angle θ. First, it is necessary to be able to find r and θ when x and y are known, or vice versa. The formulas are familiar:

$$x = r \cos \theta \qquad\qquad y = r \sin \theta$$

$$r = \sqrt{x^2 + y^2} \qquad\qquad \theta = \tan^{-1} \frac{y}{x} \qquad\qquad [53]$$

Next, it is necessary to express in polar coordinates a vector that is given in rectangular coordinates. If A_x and A_y are known, it must be

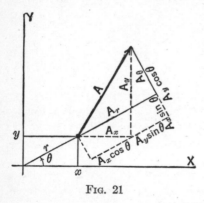

possible to find A_r and A_θ (A_r is defined as the length of the component of $\mathbf{A}$ in the radial direction, A_θ is the length of the component of $\mathbf{A}$ that is normal to A_r). Figure 21 shows the relation: at a point with coordinates (x,y) or (r,θ) there is a vector $\mathbf{A}$. The polar components of the vector, A_r and A_θ, are shown; so also are the rectangular components A_x and A_y. Two right triangles are drawn; A_x is the hypotenuse of one and A_y is the hypotenuse of the other. One angle of each triangle is θ. From the construction of the figure it may be seen that

Fig. 21

$$A_r = A_x \cos \theta + A_y \sin \theta$$
$$A_\theta = A_y \cos \theta - A_x \sin \theta \qquad\qquad [54]$$

This is the desired relation when finding polar components from rectangular components; when the polar components are known and the rectangular ones are desired, the following equations are used. They are obtained from equations 54 by simultaneous solution, or by slightly different construction in Fig. 21.

$$A_x = A_r \cos \theta - A_\theta \sin \theta$$
$$A_y = A_r \sin \theta + A_\theta \cos \theta \qquad\qquad [55]$$

Gradient in polar coordinates is now easily found. In two-dimensional rectangular coordinates it is

$$\nabla P = \mathbf{i} \frac{\partial P}{\partial x} + \mathbf{j} \frac{\partial P}{\partial y}$$

From equations 53

$$x = r \cos \theta \quad \text{and} \quad y = r \sin \theta$$

so by the rules for differentiation of a composite function (see a calculus book):

$$\frac{\partial P}{\partial x} = \frac{\partial P}{\partial r} \cos \theta - \frac{\partial P}{\partial \theta} \frac{\sin \theta}{r} \tag{56}$$

$$\frac{\partial P}{\partial y} = \frac{\partial P}{\partial r} \sin \theta + \frac{\partial P}{\partial \theta} \frac{\cos \theta}{r} \tag{57}$$

Gradient is a vector, and it is seen from the expression for ∇P that its x and y components are given by equations 56 and 57 respectively. But it is not sufficient to know the x and y components; it is necessary to find the r and θ components. This is done by means of equations 54, substituting equation 56 for the x component and equation 57 for the y component, giving the following radial and angular components:

$$(\nabla P)_r = \left(\frac{\partial P}{\partial r} \cos \theta - \frac{\partial P}{\partial \theta} \frac{\sin \theta}{r} \right) \cos \theta + \left(\frac{\partial P}{\partial r} \sin \theta + \frac{\partial P}{\partial \theta} \frac{\cos \theta}{r} \right) \sin \theta$$

$$= \frac{\partial P}{\partial r} \tag{58}$$

$$(\nabla P)_\theta = \left(\frac{\partial P}{\partial r} \sin \theta + \frac{\partial P}{\partial \theta} \frac{\cos \theta}{r} \right) \cos \theta - \left(\frac{\partial P}{\partial r} \cos \theta - \frac{\partial P}{\partial \theta} \frac{\sin \theta}{r} \right) \sin \theta$$

$$= \frac{1}{r} \frac{\partial P}{\partial \theta} \tag{59}$$

Hence, if $\mathbf{1}_r$ is a radial unit vector at any point under consideration and $\mathbf{1}_\theta$ is a unit vector normal to $\mathbf{1}_r$, gradient in two-dimensional polar coordinates is

$$\nabla P = \mathbf{1}_r \frac{\partial P}{\partial r} + \mathbf{1}_\theta \frac{1}{r} \frac{\partial P}{\partial \theta} \tag{60}$$

On page 20 the shape of a hill was described by equation 32. In polar coordinates the elevation of each point is

$$P = 1000 - r^2 \tag{61}$$

(Equation 61 may be obtained from 32 by means of 53 if the transformation is not obvious.) To find the gradient, which is the slope of the hill, use equation 60:

$$\nabla P = -\mathbf{1}_r \, 2r \tag{62}$$

Is this equivalent to the value of gradient given in equation 33, computed in rectangular coordinates?

Divergence can also be expressed in polar coordinates. Starting with rectangular coordinates, in two dimensions,

$$\nabla \cdot \mathbf{A} = \frac{\partial A_x}{\partial x} + \frac{\partial A_y}{\partial y}$$

Substituting equations 56 and 57 gives

$$\nabla \cdot \mathbf{A} = \frac{\partial A_x}{\partial r} \cos\theta - \frac{\partial A_x}{\partial \theta} \frac{\sin\theta}{r} + \frac{\partial A_y}{\partial r} \sin\theta + \frac{\partial A_y}{\partial \theta} \frac{\cos\theta}{r} \qquad [63]$$

The components of **A** must now be changed from rectangular components to polar components by means of equations 55.

$$\nabla \cdot \mathbf{A} = \frac{\partial(A_r \cos\theta - A_\theta \sin\theta)}{\partial r} \cos\theta - \frac{\partial(A_r \cos\theta - A_\theta \sin\theta)}{\partial \theta} \frac{\sin\theta}{r}$$

$$+ \frac{\partial(A_r \sin\theta + A_\theta \cos\theta)}{\partial r} \sin\theta + \frac{\partial(A_r \sin\theta + A_\theta \cos\theta)}{\partial \theta} \frac{\cos\theta}{r} \qquad [64]$$

The partial derivatives of equation 64 are now expanded, noting that θ is not a function of r but that A_r and A_θ are each functions of both r and θ. When the resulting terms are collected, the final expression for divergence is

$$\nabla \cdot \mathbf{A} = \frac{\partial A_r}{\partial r} + \frac{1}{r} \frac{\partial A_\theta}{\partial \theta} + \frac{A_r}{r} \qquad [65]$$

Curl can be expressed in polar coordinates also, and the transformation from rectangular coordinates is similar to the transformation for gradient. The resulting polar expression for curl in two dimensions is

$$\nabla \times \mathbf{A} = \mathbf{k}\left(\frac{\partial A_\theta}{\partial r} - \frac{1}{r} \frac{\partial A_r}{\partial \theta} + \frac{A_\theta}{r}\right) \qquad [66]$$

Example 4. To illustrate the use of equations 65 and 66, find divergence and curl of the vector field that is discussed in Example 3, page 27, and illustrated in Fig. 20. From the description of the field it is evident that its polar components are:

$$A_r = 1 \quad \text{and} \quad A_\theta = 0$$

From equation 65 the divergence of the field is $1/r$. Since each term of equation 66 is zero, the curl is zero. These are the same as the results found previously using rectangular coordinates, as given in equations 45 and 46, but the computation is so much simpler in polar coordinates that the advantage of their use is apparent.

TABULATION. Formulas for gradient, divergence, curl, and the Laplacian in rectangular, cylindrical, and spherical coordinates are included in Table II, inside the back cover.

PROBLEMS

1. Complete the tabulation of equation 19 to include all possible scalar and vector products of the unit vectors **i**, **j**, and **k**.

2. (a) Prove that equation 22 is correct.   (b) Prove that equation 28 is correct.

3. A farm has the shape of a parallelogram, one boundary line running east 7 miles and another directly northeast 5 miles.   Using equation 22, find the area of the farm.

4. Rain, blown by a south wind, falls at an angle of 30 degrees to the vertical at a speed of 60 feet per second.   There is 1 ounce of rain in each cubic yard of air.   How much rain falls on each square yard of the south wall of a building?   On the west wall?   On the flat roof?   Use equation 20 for this problem, representing area by a vector.

5. Draw a contour map of the hill of equation 32, and a sketch of its shape in three dimensions.   Draw vectors on the contour map to show gradient at the following points: (0,0), (0,1), (0,3), (0,−3), (3,0), (2,2), (2,1), (1,2), (−1,−2), (−2,1), (−1,2).

6. Refer to a calculus book for a proof of equation 34.

7. If, in Fig. 19b, the coordinate axes had been chosen at 45 degrees to their indicated position the field would have been defined by $\mathbf{A} = \dfrac{y - x + 10\sqrt{2}}{2}\,(\mathbf{i} + \mathbf{j})$.
Find the curl and divergence at every point using these less fortunately chosen axes.

8. $V_x = \sin y$, $V_y = 0$.   Sketch the field of V (as in Fig. 19) and find its divergence and curl.

9. $V_x = \dfrac{x}{x^2 + y^2}$ $V_y = \dfrac{y}{x^2 + y^2}$.   Sketch the field of V and find its divergence and curl.

10. Sketch contour lines of constant divergence for equation 45, and sketch the vector field of the gradient of this divergence, from equation 47.

11. Find the curl of the gradient of P in equation 32.

12. Find the divergence of the curl $[\nabla \cdot (\nabla^\times V)]$ of the vector field defined in Problem 8, using equation 39.

13. $V_x = \dfrac{1}{\sqrt{x^2 + y^2}}$ $V_y = \dfrac{1}{\sqrt{x^2 + y^2}}$:   Sketch the field defined by these equations and find its divergence and curl, and the divergence of the curl.

14. Prove that $\nabla \cdot \nabla^\times V \equiv 0$.

15. Find the Laplacian of P as given in equation 32.

16. Find the Laplacian of P if $P = -\ln r$ (r being the scalar distance of any point in a plane from a fixed point, so that by proper choice of coordinates $r^2 = x^2 + y^2$).

17. Find the Laplacian of P if $P = \dfrac{1}{r}$ (r being the scalar distance from a fixed point) in both: (a) a two-dimensional field, and (b) a three-dimensional field.

18. Prove by means of equations 53 and 54 that equation 62 is equivalent to equation 33.

19. Working from equation 44, prove that equation 66 is correct.

20. Express the field of Problem 9 in polar coordinates and find its **divergence** and curl.

21. Determine whether it is advantageous to use polar coordinates in solving Problem 13.

CHAPTER III

CERTAIN THEOREMS RELATING TO FIELDS

DIVERGENCE. The general idea of divergence was introduced in the previous chapter. Divergence occurs in a region in which lines of flow (the literal meaning of " flux lines ") appear to originate. An equation for computing divergence (equation 39) was given, but no proof or demonstration was included to show that this equation was truly related to the physical idea of divergence. Such demonstration will now be given. It will not be rigorous, but will indicate the principal steps of a rigorous proof.

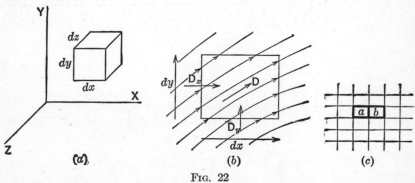

FIG. 22

Consider a small rectangular prism with its edges parallel to three coordinate axes X, Y, and Z, as in Fig. 22a. The limiting case is to be considered, in which the prism is so small that its edges are dx, dy, and dz in length. Figure 22b shows a side view of this prism, with the plane of the figure parallel to the X–Y plane. We are looking upon a side with area $dx \, dy$. Each end has area $dy \, dz$, and the top and bottom $dx \, dz$.

This small prismatic volume is located in a vector field which, for convenience, we will call $\mathbf{D}$. Flux lines of this field pass through the prism, entering through one surface and leaving through another. We wish to find how many lines, if any, originate within the volume.

Referring to Fig. 22b, the number of flux lines entering the left-hand side of the prism is equal to the area of the left-hand surface times the normal component of field strength, which is $D_x \, dy \, dz$. The number

37

leaving the right-hand surface is different if D_x changes in the distance dx. If D_x is changing at the rate $\dfrac{\partial D_x}{\partial x}$ as one passes from left to right, the amount of change in the distance dx is $\dfrac{\partial D_x}{\partial x} dx$. Hence the number of flux lines leaving the right-hand surface is $(D_x + \dfrac{\partial D_x}{\partial x} dx)\ dy\ dz$. Subtracting, the number of lines that leave the right-hand side in excess of the number that enter the left-hand side is $\dfrac{\partial D_x}{\partial x} dx\ dy\ dz$.

Similarly, the number of lines leaving the top of the prism in excess of those entering the bottom is $\dfrac{\partial D_y}{\partial y} dy\ dx\ dz$; and the number leaving the front surface is greater than the number entering the back by $\dfrac{\partial D_z}{\partial z} dz\ dx\ dy$.

Combining these quantities, the total number of flux lines leaving the volume that do not enter it is

$$\left(\frac{\partial D_x}{\partial x} + \frac{\partial D_y}{\partial y} + \frac{\partial D_z}{\partial z} \right) dx\ dy\ dz$$

But divergence is defined as the number of flux lines originating per unit volume, so if the volume of the prism is dv,

$$\nabla \cdot \mathbf{D} = \left(\frac{\partial D_x}{\partial x} + \frac{\partial D_y}{\partial y} + \frac{\partial D_z}{\partial z} \right) \frac{dx\ dy\ dz}{dv}$$

Since the volume of the prism, dv, is equal to $dx\ dy\ dz$ it follows that

$$\nabla \cdot \mathbf{D} = \frac{\partial D_x}{\partial x} + \frac{\partial D_y}{\partial y} + \frac{\partial D_z}{\partial z} \qquad [67]$$

and this is equation 39.

GAUSS's THEOREM. Now consider that space is divided into an unlimited number of small cells of volume dv, as in Fig. 22c. The number of flux lines leaving one such cell, marked a in the figure, is greater than the number entering that cell by $\nabla \cdot \mathbf{D}\, dv$. The number originating within the adjoining cell b is likewise the divergence at that location times the volume of that cell. The number of lines emanating from the two cells together, considered as a unit, is the sum of the two products of divergence and volume. Adding more cells to the group thus begun, the number of lines of flux issuing from any volume is greater than the number entering that volume by the summation (or integral) of all the individual products of divergence and volume. Hence

$$\text{Excess outward flux} = \int \nabla \cdot \mathbf{D} \, dv \qquad [68]$$

In Chapter I, flux of the vector field $\mathbf{D}$ passing through an area $\mathbf{a}$ was defined as

$$\int \mathbf{D} \cdot da \qquad [9]$$

and from this it follows that the net flux passing outward through any closed surface (the excess of the outward flux over the inward flux) is found by integrating over the whole closed surface:[1]

$$\oint \mathbf{D} \cdot da \qquad [69]$$

Now equation 69 and equation 68 are different expressions for the same quantity of flux and hence may be equated, giving

$$\oint \mathbf{D} \cdot da = \int \nabla \cdot \mathbf{D} \, dv \qquad [70]$$

This is a theorem of great importance. It relates the integral of divergence within any volume to the integral of the vector field strength over the surface enclosing that volume. It is sometimes called the divergence theorem and sometimes (although not quite properly) *Gauss's theorem*.

A number of illustrations of the application of this theorem are given in the preceding chapter, especially with reference to Fig. 15.

CURL. The idea of curl was developed in Chapter II with reference to a hypothetical paddle-wheel in a vector field of fluid velocity. Rotation of the paddle-wheel occurred when the summation of the components of field strength tangential to the paddle-wheel's circumference failed to add to zero. This was illustrated by reference to the force exerted on specific paddles, a painfully crude illustration. The idea

---

[1] Two comments regarding notation: A small circle superimposed on the integral sign indicates integration over a closed path, either a closed line or a closed surface, depending upon whether the integration is with respect to distance or area, as indicated by the nature of the differential quantity. In this case da indicates that the integration is over an area, and the circle upon the integral sign indicates that the surface over which the integral is taken must be a closed surface.

In equation 3 the differential quantity ds, s being distance, indicates integration along a line; that it must be a closed line is shown by the circle on the integral sign.

The area da is a vector quantity, as discussed in Chapter II. The direction of the vector da is normal to the area and, *by convention*, it is *outward*. It is obvious that this convention is useful only for a closed surface.

of curl is much better formulated in terms of the *circulation* of the vector field about the periphery of the paddle-wheel.   The paddle-wheel may then be removed entirely, leaving curl defined in terms of the circulation about a small closed path.

The mathematical quantity **circulation** is the line-integral of a vector field along a given path.   If the vector field is **E** its circulation about a closed path is

$$\oint \mathbf{E} \cdot d\mathbf{s}$$

This is merely a mathematical expression of the ordinary concept of circulation, as of air or water, and it is clearly the circulation of fluid about its periphery that makes a paddle-wheel turn.

Curl is a microscopic circulation. Consider the exploring paddle-wheel in a vector field, and orient it so that its speed of rotation is maximum.   (This determines the orientation in which the circulation around its circumference is maximum.)   Now allow the paddle-wheel to vanish, but retain its circumference as a circular path in space.   The circulation of the vector field about this path (found from the above definition) depends upon the area enclosed within the path.   Dividing circulation by area gives a ratio that is substantially independent of the size or shape of the path provided the path is small.   This ratio is

$$\frac{\text{Circulation about a small closed path}}{\text{Area of surface bounded by that path}}$$

The limit approached by this ratio as the path is allowed to shrink to a mere point is the **curl** at that point.

Curl is thus the limiting value of *circulation per unit area*.   It follows that the circulation of a vector field around a closed path of infinitesimal size depends upon the curl of the field at that point and the infinitesimal area within the path.   But the circulation about a small closed path also depends upon its orientation.   Curl must be treated as a vector quantity.   The direction of the curl vector is defined as normal to the plane in which circulation is maximum, and the circulation about an infinitesimal closed path in either that or any other plane is the scalar product of the curl vector and the area vector: $(\nabla \times \mathbf{E}) \cdot d\mathbf{a}$.

Now curl has been defined in terms of circulation.   To find an expression for curl in terms of the vector field itself we determine the circulation about a small closed path in the vector field.   It is not necessary that such a path be circular.   Let us assume a small rectangular closed path, as in Fig. 23*a*, located in the X–Y plane.   It is desired to find the circulation about it, and this is done (in accordance with the definition of circulation) by multiplying the length of each side of the rectangle by the component of field strength parallel to that side. The lengths of the sides are (in the limiting case) dx and dy. Starting at the lower left corner in Fig. 23a, consider the bottom of the rectangle: the length is dx, in a positive direction, and the component of the field along the bottom of the rectangle is $E_{x \text{ at } y_1}$. The bottom of the rectangle therefore provides the first term of the following expression for circulation, the other three terms being obtained from the other three sides of the rectangle taken in order, counterclockwise:

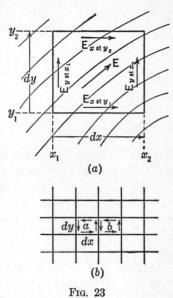

(a)

(b)

FIG. 23

$$\text{Circulation} = E_{x \text{ at } y_1} \, dx + E_{y \text{ at } x_2} \, dy \\ - E_{x \text{ at } y_2} \, dx - E_{y \text{ at } x_1} \, dy \quad [71]$$

The third and fourth terms are negative because, in maintaining a counterclockwise direction about the rectangle, the top and left-hand side are traversed in a negative direction. The distance traveled along the top is $-dx$, and along the left side, $-dy$.

Regrouping terms,

$$\text{Circulation} = (E_{y \text{ at } x_2} - E_{y \text{ at } x_1}) \, dy - (E_{x \text{ at } y_2} - E_{x \text{ at } y_1}) \, dx \quad [72]$$

The first parenthesis of the right-hand member is the amount by which E_y increases in the distance dx between x_1 and x_2; it is therefore equal to $\frac{\partial E_y}{\partial x} \, dx$. The quantity in the second parenthesis is similar, and corresponds to the change of E_x in the distance y_1 to y_2. Hence equation 72 may be written

$$\text{Circulation} = \left(\frac{\partial E_y}{\partial x} \, dx\right) dy - \left(\frac{\partial E_x}{\partial y} \, dy\right) dx$$

Since, as seen above, circulation about an infinitesimal path is equal to $(\nabla \times E) \cdot da$, a being the area within the path, we may write

$$(\nabla \times E) \cdot da = \frac{\partial E_y}{\partial x} \, dx \, dy - \frac{\partial E_x}{\partial y} \, dy \, dx \quad [73]$$

The differential area within the rectangular path is equal to $dx \, dy$, and both sides of the equation may be divided by this quantity. Since da represents an area in the X–Y plane, equation 73 gives the component of curl normal to that plane. In the two-dimensional field this is the total curl, and

$$\nabla^\times \mathbf{E} = \mathbf{k}\left(\frac{\partial E_y}{\partial x} - \frac{\partial E_x}{\partial y}\right) \qquad [74]$$

This is identical with equation 44. In a three-dimensional field this is one component only, the complete expression for curl being given by equation 40.

STOKES' THEOREM. The discussion of the previous section concerns curl at a single point, or the region within an infinitesimal rectangle. It is now desired to determine the integral of curl over a surface of finite extent. This may be done by finding curl at every point of the surface and integrating. But there is a very helpful theorem, due to Stokes, that frequently saves a good deal of trouble.

Consider the small rectangle marked a in Fig. 23b, assumed to be in a vector field. There is circulation around this rectangle, as indicated by the arrows, corresponding to curl of the vector field within the area a. Now consider the adjoining rectangle marked b. There is circulation about this rectangle also, corresponding to curl in the area b. But since the rectangles a and b have one side in common this contributes a certain amount of circulation in one rectangle and an exactly equal but opposite amount in the other. Therefore the sum of the curl in rectangle a plus the curl in rectangle b can be found by measuring the circulation around the outer perimeter of the larger rectangle made up of both a and b together, and giving no further attention to the equal and opposite components contributed by the common side.

Other rectangles may be added to these two, in any number. Always the circulation along common sides may be discarded, so that no matter how large the final area or what its shape, the summation of curl at all points of a surface is equal to the circulation about the perimeter of the surface. Mathematically, the line integral of a vector, which defines circulation, may be equated to the surface integral of the curl of the vector, and the result is Stokes' theorem:

$$\oint \mathbf{E} \cdot d\mathbf{s} = \int (\nabla^\times \mathbf{E}) \cdot d\mathbf{a} \qquad [75]$$

This theorem is not limited to a plane surface. Although the above discussion has been illustrated by reference to the plane surface of Fig. 23, the theorem applies and can be rigorously proved for a surface of any shape. The surface over which curl is integrated in equation 75 might, for example, be concave like a cup or a kettle. In the latter case the integration of curl all over the kettle would be equal to the circulation around the rim of the kettle.

But suppose the kettle has a lid, placed upon the kettle in the usual manner. The rim of the lid and the rim of the kettle coincide. Hence the integration of curl over the lid must be equal to the integration of curl over the kettle. That is to say, in more abstract terms, the integration of curl over a surface in a vector field, as indicated by the right-hand member of equation 75, is the same for all surfaces having a common perimeter, and is quite independent of the shape of the surface.

COMPARISON OF THEOREMS. Gauss's theorem and Stokes' theorem are very similar in their essential natures, for they relate large-scale phenomena to small-scale phenomena — the macroscopic to the microscopic.

If a vector field is examined minutely at a particular point, as with a microscope, it will be found to have a certain divergence at that point. This examination is performed, as a matter of fact, not with a microscope, but with a partial derivative, and equation 67 gives the divergence when the partial derivatives at the point are known.

But divergence has a large-scale result that can be detected without the aid of a microscope (or a partial derivative). This is flux: if flux issues from a volume there is divergence within that volume, and Gauss's theorem gives the relation. One side of Gauss's theorem is in terms of the field passing through a surface; this is a surface of finite size, and is the macroscopic quantity. The other side of the theorem is in terms of the divergence throughout a volume; this must be considered point by point, and is the microscopic quantity.

Similarly, Stokes' theorem relates the macroscopic effect, circulation along a closed path, to the microscopic phenomenon, curl at every point of a surface bounded by that path.

These theorems are frequently useful when the microscopic nature of a field is known and the macroscopic nature is desired (that is, when one knows the derivatives and wishes to find the field) or vice versa. Such applications will be illustrated in the next chapter, in which our study of the electric field is continued.

SCALAR POTENTIAL. The scalar field of elevation-above-sea-level is a **potential** field. It is a field of gravitational potential. Its value at any point is defined as the work required to move a body of unit mass to that point from sea level, or as the amount of potential energy gained by the body in being so moved.

A level surface — or, more precisely, a surface of constant elevation above sea level — is an **equipotential surface,** for a body can be moved from one point to another of such a surface without any change of gravitational potential, and without any work being done. Equipotential surfaces near sea level are shown in Fig. 24a, and equipotential surfaces at greater distances from the earth in Fig. 24b.

The **gravitational field** is a field of force. It is therefore a vector field. Its value at each point is equal, by definition, to the gravitational force on a body of unit mass at that point. It is a field directed downward, toward the center of the earth.

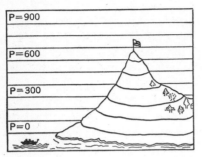

FIG. 24

Gravitational potential is defined in terms of work, and the gravitational field in terms of force, so there is a simple relation between them. The field is the negative of the *gradient* of the potential:

$$\mathbf{F} = -\nabla P \qquad [76]$$

Although written with reference to the gravitational field, this equation expresses a general relation between potential and force. The force field may be found from the potential field by differentiation. Every potential field has a gradient, and **F** can always be found from P. But it is not always possible, knowing a field of force, to find a corresponding potential field; a potential field does not always exist. Fortunately there is a simple criterion by which we may know whether there is a potential field corresponding to a given field of force.

It was shown in Chapter II that if a vector field is the gradient of some scalar field, the vector field has no curl. The converse of this theorem provides us with the desired criterion: *If a vector field is found to have no curl, that vector field is the gradient of some scalar field.* Symbolically,

$$\text{If } \nabla{\times}\mathbf{F} = 0 \quad \text{then } \mathbf{F} = -\nabla P \qquad [77]$$

This says that if a vector field has no curl, some scalar field exists whose gradient is everywhere identical with the given vector field; it does not tell how to find that scalar field, but it does give assurance of its existence. When the scalar field P is found to exist it is called a *potential* field.

The electrostatic field offers an example.   As will be seen in the next chapter, the electrostatic field has no curl.   Therefore we know from the above corollary that an electrostatic potential field exists.   Indeed, it is well known that electrostatic potential exists, and that voltage is electrostatic potential difference.

The static magnetic field has no curl in regions that are not carrying current.   This will be discussed in Chapter VII.   Hence if a wire is carrying current there is a magnetic field, around that wire, which has no curl.   A scalar field of magnetic potential can be found in the space around the wire.   (If the wire is straight, the equipotential surfaces of this magnetic scalar-potential field will be radial planes.)   But *within* the wire, where current is flowing, there will be a magnetic field of which the curl is not zero.   Within the wire, then, no field of magnetic scalar potential can be found.[2]

As another example, flow of heat through a solid body is a vector field that has no curl.   Therefore a scalar field of heat potential must exist.   It does; it is temperature, and the gradient of temperature is a vector field proportional to heat flow.

In the gravitational field, one surface will contain all points at sea level (Potential = 0) and another all points 100 feet above sea level (Potential = 100) and so on.   (See Fig. 24a and b.)   By these equipotential surfaces all space is divided into thin plates or shells called lamellas.

Only vector fields without curl have this characteristic of dividing space into lamellas (thin laminations) by means of equipotential surfaces, so, following the usage of James Clerk Maxwell, a vector field without curl is called a **lamellar** field.   Sometimes a lamellar field is called **irrotational** because it has no curl.

SOLENOIDAL FIELDS AND VECTOR POTENTIAL.   It was also seen in Chapter II that if a vector field is the curl of another vector field, it has no divergence.   Expressed in symbols:

$$\text{If } \mathbf{B} = \nabla \times \mathbf{A} \quad \text{then } \nabla \cdot \mathbf{B} = 0 \qquad [78]$$

This theorem also has its converse: *If a vector field has no divergence, that vector field is the curl of some other vector field.*   Symbolically,

$$\text{If } \nabla \cdot \mathbf{B} = 0 \quad \text{then } \mathbf{B} = \nabla \times \mathbf{A} \qquad [79]$$

In other words, if the vector field **B** has no divergence (as is true, for

---

[2] The physical meaning of this is that if a magnetic pole could be placed within the conductor (the conductor may be visualized as being mercury) the work done in moving the magnetic pole from one point to another would depend upon the path followed, and no value of potential can be assigned.

instance, in a field that represents the velocity of flow of an incompressible liquid) then some other vector field can be found, which we choose to call **A**, such that the curl of A is everywhere equal to **B**. At least, it is to be hoped that the field **A** can be found. The process of finding it is sometimes difficult, and sometimes impossible, but if **A** exists, whether or not its computation is feasible, it is given the name of **vector potential.**

The vector potential is somewhat analogous to the scalar potential of the previous section. Nevertheless, it must be emphasized that it is an entirely different quantity. If a vector field has neither curl nor divergence it will have both a scalar potential and a vector potential, and they will be different quantities with little resemblance to each other.

A vector field without divergence is called **solenoidal.** The name means that all the lines of flux are closed curves, having neither beginning nor end, a fact that follows necessarily from there being no divergence. Every solenoidal field has a vector potential. All magnetic fields are solenoidal, and therefore there is always a magnetic vector potential.

Example. Figure 16a, page 22, shows water circulating in a tub. It might equally well be interpreted as the magnetic field within a conductor of circular cross section. Assume a set of cylindrical coordinates; this is a three-dimensional set in which r is radial distance from an axis, z is distance parallel to the axis, and θ is angle as in polar coordinates (equation 53). The system of coordinates should be assumed with its axis coinciding with the axis of rotation of Fig. 16a; it is then the simplest and best adapted system to use for a problem of this character. (Formulas in terms of cylindrical coordinates are given in Table II.)

The field of Fig. 16a, whether considered to be velocity of water or magnetic field strength, is described by the equations

$$H_r = 0$$
$$H_\theta = ar \qquad [80]$$
$$H_z = 0$$

where a is a known constant. It is desired to determine the scalar and vector potentials of this field.

To determine whether a scalar potential exists, find the curl of the given field **H**. Since **H** is essentially two-dimensional, equation 66 is adequate (or the complete expression for curl in Table II may be used) and the result is

$$\nabla \times \mathbf{H} = \mathbf{k}\left(a\frac{\partial r}{\partial r} - 0 + \frac{ar}{r}\right) = \mathbf{k}\,2a \qquad [81]$$

Hence the curl is not zero, the field is not lamellar, and it is useless to try to find a scalar-potential field, for none exists.

To determine whether a vector potential exists, find the divergence of **H**. Using equation 65, each term of which is zero, it is evident that the field does not have divergence, and hence it should be possible to find a vector potential. Let us call the assumed vector-potential field **A**, and try to find what it is.

The curl of **A** must be **H**, so if little paddle-wheels — the " curl-meters" of Fig. 18 — are placed with their axes along lines of **H**, as in Fig. 25, they must be turned at proper relative speed by the vector-potential field **A**. (As an alternative way of considering the problem, if all the curl-meters of Fig. 25 are driven at the proper speed, in proportion to the strength of **H** along their axes, they will act as pumps and, by churning the hypothetical liquid in

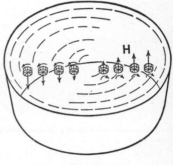

Fig. 25

which they are supposed to be, they will impart to it a velocity equivalent to the vector-potential field **A**.)

Now, by consideration of Fig. 25, it becomes clear that one possible solution for vector potential would be a vertical field that has zero intensity in the center of the tub and that increases in vertically downward intensity nearer the sides. This would spin all the curl-meters in the proper direction, and suggests a vector-potential field parallel to the Z axis. The strength of this vector-potential field will vary with radius, but since it will presumably be symmetrical it will not vary with either θ or z. The manner in which the vector potential varies with radius is unknown, but we may hope that it can be expressed by a power series[3] and write for the vector potential **A**:

$$A_r = 0$$
$$A_\theta = 0 \qquad\qquad [82]$$
$$A_z = b_0 + b_1 r + b_2 r^2 + b_3 r^3 + \cdots$$

This expression for **A** is correct if it is possible to find values of the coefficients b_0, b_1, b_2, and so on, that will make the curl of **A** equal **H**.

[3] This illustrates an extremely powerful method of solving differential equations. When the solution is an unknown function it is very often possible to substitute for it an appropriate series (in many cases a power series) with undetermined coefficients. The coefficients are then evaluated from the differential equation, and the result will be the solution in terms of a series which may or may not be recognized as a familiar function.

Using the expression for curl in cylindrical coordinates that is given in Table II, and substituting into it values from equation 82,

$$\nabla \times A = 1_r \frac{1}{r} \frac{\partial A_z}{\partial \theta} - 1_\theta \frac{\partial A_z}{\partial r} \qquad [83]$$

The first term of this expression is zero, for A_z does not vary with θ, and the radial component of the curl of A vanishes:

$$(\nabla \times A)_r = 0 \qquad [84]$$

The second term of equation 83 gives as the theta component of curl:

$$(\nabla \times A)_\theta = -(b_1 + 2b_2 r + 3b_3 r^2 + \cdots) \qquad [85]$$

The axial component of the curl of A is zero since it contains only derivatives of A_r and A_θ, both of which are zero:

$$(\nabla \times A)_z = 0 \qquad [86]$$

In order that A may be the vector potential of H, the three components of the curl of A must be equal to the three corresponding components of H. The radial and axial components agree, as shown by comparison of equations 84 and 86 with equations 80. For the angular components to agree it is necessary that

$$-(b_1 + 2b_2 r + 3b_3 r^2 + \cdots) \equiv ar$$

This is written as an identity because it must be true for all values of the variable r. It will be true for all values of r if and only if

$$-2b_2 = a$$

and

$$b_1 = b_3 = b_4 = \cdots = 0$$

Hence, referring back to equation 82, a complete and correct expression for vector potential is

$$A_r = 0$$
$$A_\theta = 0 \qquad [87]$$
$$A_z = b_0 - \frac{a}{2} r^2$$

and the problem is solved. It is interesting that b_0 can have any constant value[4] without affecting the requirement that the curl of A equal H. It is of the nature of a constant of integration.

---

[4] Indeed any irrotational function may be added to A, for the curl of any irrotational function is zero.

PROBLEMS

1. Derive an expression for curl in polar coordinates, as in equation 66. Do not merely transform from an expression in rectangular coordinates, but start by summing circulation around an area such as that shown in the accompanying figure.

2. Figure 19a shows a vector field which, being without curl, must have a scalar potential. Assuming the potential at the origin of coordinates to be zero, find the potential at all other points. On a sketch of the field, draw lines (equipotential lines) connecting points of equal potential.

3. Study Fig. 19b to determine whether equipotential lines can be drawn. Is there curl?

4. Does the vector field of Fig. 20 have a scalar-potential field? Can you determine it?

PROB. 1

5. Gravitational potential is inversely proportional to distance from the center of the earth. What is the nature of the gravitational field, using equation 76?

6. Do equipotential surfaces exist within the canal of Fig. 17 (surfaces that define the scalar potential of the indicated velocity field)? Can you locate them?

7. A vector field V is defined by $V_x = 10$, $V_y = V_z = 0$. Find its scalar-potential field. Find its vector-potential field. Both vector and scalar potential are to be zero at the origin of coordinates.

8. Consider the possible existence of a vector field with zero divergence and zero curl at all points. Then impose the further restriction that the field strength must not anywhere be infinite. Then require also that the field strength be zero at an infinite distance in all directions.

Chapter IV

THE ELECTROSTATIC FIELD

In Chapter I four experiments were described. In order to be useful, the results of these experiments were expressed in mathematical form as equations 2, 3, and 7. Equation 2 relates the force on a charged exploring particle to the electric field strength:

$$\mathbf{F} = Q\mathbf{E} \tag{2}$$

Equation 3 states that the line integral of the electrostatic field about any closed path is zero:

$$\oint \mathbf{E} \cdot d\mathbf{s} = 0 \tag{3}$$

Equation 7 states that the total flux leaving any closed surface is proportional to the excess positive charge within that surface:

$$\oint \mathbf{D} \cdot da = \oint \kappa \mathbf{E} \cdot da = 4\pi Q \tag{7}$$

Equation 2 is found to be true *at all points*.

Equation 3 is found to be true along *every possible* closed path of integration.

Equation 7 is found to be true over *every possible* closed surface of integration.

Equations 2, 3, and 7 contain all necessary knowledge of electrostatics. No further experimentation is needed to develop the science of electrostatics in free space or isotropic material. Mathematical manipulation based on these equations will determine any electrostatic field when the charges that produce that field are known. The mathematics, however, is rarely easy. This chapter will be devoted to the fundamental principles of the mathematical solution, followed by a few examples.

Consider, first, equation 3. Applying Stokes' theorem (equation 75) gives:

$$\oint \mathbf{E} \cdot d\mathbf{s} = \int (\nabla \times \mathbf{E}) \cdot da = 0 \tag{88}$$

The conclusion from this equation is that the electrostatic field has no curl. This conclusion would not result from any single measurement that gave a value of zero for the line integral of **E** around some one closed path, for such an experimental result would not preclude the possibility that curl might exist at various points in the field even though the integral of curl over the surface of integration of equation 88 chanced to be zero. But it was specially emphasized that equation 3 applies to *all* closed paths, and therefore equation 88 applies to *all* surfaces, and the only way that equation 88 can apply to all surfaces of integration is for the curl of **E** to be zero everywhere. Hence

$$\nabla \times \mathbf{E} = 0 \qquad [89]$$

It follows from equation 89 that the electrostatic field is lamellar, and an electrostatic potential exists. If potential is called V, the electric field will (by equation 76) be the gradient of V (with a negative sign) so that

$$\mathbf{E} = -\nabla V \qquad [90]$$

Often in the solution of an electrostatic problem V can be found. It is then easy to find **E** by means of equation 90.

Another fundamental relation is expressed by equation 7. Applying Gauss's theorem to this equation gives

$$\oint \mathbf{D} \cdot d\mathbf{a} = \int (\nabla \cdot \mathbf{D}) \, dv = 4\pi \, Q \qquad [91]$$

In any region in which there is no electric charge, so $Q = 0$, $\int (\nabla \cdot \mathbf{D}) \, dv = 0$ and hence the divergence of **D** is zero.

But where charge is not zero divergence is not zero. It is convenient to express divergence in terms of the density of electric charge (charge per unit volume) which may be called ρ. The charge within a closed surface is equal to the integral of the charge density through the contained volume. If the charge Q in equation 91 is expressed as $\int \rho \, dv$ the equation becomes

$$\int (\nabla \cdot \mathbf{D}) \, dv = 4\pi \int \rho \, dv \qquad [92]$$

The two integrals of this equation are both volume integrals. Moreover, they are integrals throughout the same volume: through the volume, that is, contained within a specified closed surface. Finally, that closed surface is purely arbitrary; it may be any closed surface, of any size, shape, or location. Equation 92 can be true under this variety of conditions only if the integrand on one side of the equation equals the integrand on the other; if, that is,

$$\nabla \cdot \mathbf{D} = 4\pi \, \rho \tag{93}$$

Within a homogeneous material, where κ does not change from point to point, this can be written

$$\nabla \cdot \mathbf{E} = \frac{4\pi}{\kappa} \, \rho \tag{94}$$

This is an expression that relates electric field to charge density. It is also possible to relate electric potential to charge density by substituting equation 90 into 94, giving:

$$\nabla \cdot (\nabla V) = - \frac{4\pi}{\kappa} \, \rho$$

or

$$\nabla^2 V = - \frac{4\pi}{\kappa} \, \rho \tag{95}$$

When the meaning of the operator *nabla* is considered, it is evident that this is a second-order partial differential equation. It is of such importance that it is given a name: it is **Poisson's equation.** In the special case that applies to space containing no charge it reduces to

$$\nabla^2 V = 0 \tag{96}$$

This is an even more famous differential equation, called **Laplace's equation.**

The study of electrostatics is essentially the solution of these equations. To sum up:

$$\mathbf{E} = -\nabla V \tag{90}$$

$$\nabla^2 V = - \frac{4\pi}{\kappa} \, \rho \tag{95}$$

These relations completely define an electrostatic field, and their application to specific problems will now be considered.

CONDUCTORS. A conducting material is one in which electric charge can flow. Conducting materials contain electricity that is free to move when it is acted upon by the force of an electric field, and this is true even though they are " uncharged " in the sense of having no excess of either sign of charge.

Since charge can flow within a conductor, there can be no electrostatic field within the conducting material, for if there were it would exert force on the charge and move it from one point to another until the electric field was reduced to zero by the redistribution of the charge. Hence, within a conductor, in the electro*static* case:

$$\mathbf{E} = 0$$

from which: [97]

$$V \text{ is constant}$$

Since $\mathbf{E}$ is zero it follows that $\nabla \cdot \mathbf{E} = 0$, and hence that $\rho = 0$. Therefore there can be no electric charge at any point within the material of a conductor. But $\mathbf{E}$ is not necessarily zero at the surface of a conducting body, and electric charge may be located on the surface. The conclusion is that all the charge on a conducting body will flow to the surface and remain there.

Certain general conclusions may be drawn about the electrostatic field in space just beyond the surface of a conductor. Since the entire conductor is at the same potential (equation 97) the surface of the conductor is an equipotential surface. The electric field is always normal to equipotential surfaces; electric field is the potential *gradient,* and gradient is always normal to the equipotential surfaces of the field from which it is derived, as considered in Chapter II. The electrostatic field at the surface of any conductor will therefore be normal to the surface of the conductor.

The previous paragraph gives the direction of the field at the conductor surface; something may also be said about the strength of the field. Since charge on the conducting body is distributed over the surface it is convenient to speak of the density of charge in terms of charge per unit area. As ρ was used in equation 92 to represent charge per unit volume, σ will now be used to represent charge per unit area of surface, and total charge is found from

$$\int \sigma \, da = Q \tag{98}$$

If the charge density per unit area of a conducting surface is σ there must be $4\pi \, \sigma$ flux lines extending normally outward from each unit area. This follows from the fact that 4π lines emanate from each unit of positive charge. The electrostatic flux density in space just outside a charged conducting surface is therefore 4π times the density of charge on the surface, and in direction it is normal to the surface. $\mathbf{D}$ is flux density, and its normal component at the surface (which may be written D_n) is

$$D_n = \kappa \, E_n = 4\pi \, \sigma \tag{99}$$

So if the distribution of charge on the surface of a conductor is known, the electric field just outside the conductor can be found. Similarly, if the field is known the charge distribution can be found. Ordinarily, however, neither is known, and both must be found from the fact that the conductor surface is an equipotential surface with a known total charge, which makes the solution more complicated.

A CHARGED SPHERE. Consider an isolated spherical conductor with a known charge Q upon it. Find the electric field about the sphere, in space that is filled with material of dielectric constant κ.

The problem may be solved by finding a potential field that satisfies Laplace's equation

$$\nabla^2 V = 0$$

and at the same time satisfies the boundary conditions that (1) the surface of the sphere is an equipotential surface and (2) the total charge on the sphere is Q.

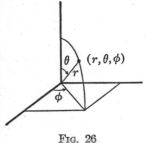

The expansion of Laplace's equation in rectangular coordinates was given in equation 51, but for use in a problem concerning a sphere it will be much more convenient to expand in spherical coordinates. In using spherical coordinates, each point in space is located by a radial distance r and two angles θ and ϕ, as in Fig. 26. The derivation of the

FIG. 26

Laplacian in spherical coordinates will not be given here (it may be found in advanced calculus books); the result is included in Table II (inside back cover). It is

$$\nabla^2 V = \frac{\partial^2 V}{\partial r^2} + \frac{1}{r^2} \frac{\partial^2 V}{\partial \theta^2} + \frac{1}{r^2 \sin^2 \theta} \frac{\partial^2 V}{\partial \phi^2} + \frac{2}{r} \frac{\partial V}{\partial r} + \frac{\cot \theta}{r^2} \frac{\partial V}{\partial \theta} \quad [100]$$

A solution of our problem, then, is an expression for potential that will make equation 100 equal zero and that at the same time will make the surface of the conducting sphere an equipotential surface.

Fortunately, the problem can be greatly simplified by consideration of symmetry. Since our charged sphere is isolated in space, whatever happens on or about the sphere must be independent of any direction except radial direction. No other direction can be defined. To distinguish any other direction it would be necessary to have another object in space, for comparison.

So, if there is no distinction between different directions, the electric potential V about the sphere cannot be different in different directions. It must be the same for all values of θ and ϕ (referring to Fig. 26 and assuming the center of the charged sphere at the origin of coordinates), varying only when r is changed.

Since V is a function of r only, and does not vary with θ or ϕ, Laplace's equation reduces to

$$\nabla^2 V = \frac{\partial^2 V}{\partial r^2} + \frac{2}{r}\frac{\partial V}{\partial r} = 0 \qquad [101]$$

Now this is an ordinary differential equation that is reducible to a linear equation with constant coefficients. The solution is

$$V = \frac{a}{r} + b \qquad [102]$$

in which a and b are any arbitrary constants. To check the correctness of this solution it may be substituted back into equation 100 which is thereby reduced to an identity.

Next, a and b must be evaluated from boundary conditions. Assume that the potential at a very great distance from the sphere is unaffected by the charge on the sphere, so that when $r = \infty$, $V = 0$. Substituting these values into equation 102 gives $b = 0$, and the equation reduces to

$$V = \frac{a}{r} \qquad [103]$$

The remaining constant, a, must be evaluated in terms of the charge on the sphere.

First, the radius of the sphere must be known; let it be r_0. Since the charge Q must be distributed symmetrically over the entire surface of the sphere, the charge per unit area, σ, is

$$\sigma = \frac{Q}{4\pi\, r_0^2}$$

and from equation 99 it follows that the field strength at the surface of the sphere, radial in direction, will be

$$E = \frac{4\pi}{\kappa}\, \frac{Q}{4\pi\, r_0^2} = \frac{Q}{\kappa\, r_0^2} \qquad [104]$$

Now since potential does not vary with θ or ϕ, the potential gradient is everywhere radial, and the magnitude of the electric field strength at any point is found[1] as

$$E = -\frac{\partial V}{\partial r} = \frac{a}{r^2} \qquad [105]$$

---

[1] See expression for gradient in spherical coordinates in Table II.

This is true everywhere, so it is true at the surface of the sphere, and equating 105 to 104 with the provision that $r = r_0$:

$$\frac{a}{r_0{}^2} = \frac{Q}{\kappa\, r_0{}^2}$$

from which $a = Q/\kappa$. Finally, then, at any point external to the charged sphere

$$V = \frac{Q}{\kappa\, r} \quad \text{and} \quad E = \frac{Q}{\kappa\, r^2} \tag{106}$$

The physical interpretation of these quantities may well be repeated. E, the electric field, is a force; it is equal at any point to the force on an exploring particle with unit positive charge. V, the potential, represents work; the potential of a point in space is the work required to move to that point an exploring particle with unit positive charge, starting an infinite distance away.

The electric field is everywhere away from a positively charged body, because the force on a positive exploring particle will be repulsive; and potential increases as one approaches a positively charged body, because one must do work in moving an exploring particle against the force of the electric field.

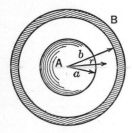

FIG. 27

SPHERICAL CONDENSER. A charged conducting sphere A of radius a is concentrically located within a hollow conducting sphere B of inside radius b, as in Fig. 27. The electric field in the free space between spheres A and B is identical with the field in the same region about an isolated sphere similar to A and with the same charge. It is radial in direction, and its strength is

$$E = \frac{Q}{r^2} \tag{107}$$

The outer sphere B carries an electric charge equal and opposite to that on A, and the electric field terminates on the inner surface of B. The two spheres constitute a condenser; it has capacitance, and there is voltage between the spheres.

Voltage, which is essentially *potential difference* between two points (ordinarily between two metallic conductors), is defined as

$$V_{12} = \int_1^2 \mathbf{E} \cdot d\mathbf{s} \tag{108}$$

That is, voltage from point 1 to point 2 is the line integral of the electric field along any path from point 1 to point 2. This is the amount by which point 1 is at a higher potential than point 2.

It is interesting to notice that potential difference or voltage between two points is the work that will be done by electric force on a unit electric charge that is allowed to move from one point to the other. Substituting equation 2 in equation 108,

$$V_{12} = \frac{1}{Q} \int_1^2 \mathbf{F} \cdot d\mathbf{s}$$

and since the integral of force times distance is work,

$$V_{12} = \frac{W_{12}}{Q}$$

Voltage between spheres of the spherical condenser is found by locating a point 1 on the surface of A and a point 2 on the surface of B. The integration to determine voltage is simplest if 1 and 2 are on the same radial line, for then the line of integration is parallel to the electric field and all the distances are radial. In that case

$$V_{AB} = \int_a^b E \, dr = \int_a^b \frac{Q}{r^2} \, dr = \frac{Q(b-a)}{ab} \qquad [109]$$

Capacitance of a condenser is, by definition, the charge divided by the voltage.

$$C = \frac{Q}{V} \qquad [110]$$

The capacitance of the spherical condenser is therefore very simply

$$C = \frac{ab}{b-a} \qquad [111]$$

a quantity that is determined entirely by the geometry of the condenser.

Occasionally one encounters references to the capacitance of an isolated sphere. This may be considered to be the limit approached by the capacitance of the spherical condenser as the outer sphere is allowed to become large without limit. Letting b in equation 111 approach infinity, we obtain as the limiting value of capacitance:

$$C = a$$

INVERSE SQUARE LAW. There is a radial electric field about a sphere with charge Q_1, the strength of which is given by equation 106 as

$$E_1 = \frac{Q_1}{r^2} \qquad [112]$$

A second charged sphere, with charge Q_2, is moved into the electric field of the first sphere. It is required to find the force exerted on the second sphere by the electric field of the first.

By equation 2,

$$F = Q_2 E_1 \qquad [113]$$

and if the distance from the center of one sphere to the center of the other is r, equation 112 gives

$$F = \frac{Q_1 Q_2}{r^2} \qquad [114]$$

This is the well-known **Coulomb's law**. Historically, it was discovered in the latter part of the eighteenth century, by direct experiment by Coulomb, who used his newly invented torsion balance. Much of the science of electrostatics was deduced from it. In the present discussion, however, Coulomb's law is itself deduced from the experiments described in Chapter I.

There is one important provision to be made in connection with equation 114. It is accurate only if the two charged spheres are so far apart that neither disturbs the distribution of charge on the surface of the other. For if the charge on the first sphere were redistributed to any noticeable extent by the electrostatic attraction or repulsion of Q_2, the electric field about the sphere would no longer be strictly radial at all points. Perfect symmetry would not, then, exist. If the radius of each sphere is small compared with the spacing between spheres no appreciable disturbance will take place and equation 114 will be accurate. For mathematical rigor the limiting case is considered: the charges Q_1 and Q_2 are assumed concentrated at points, rather than being distributed on spheres. But this has the disadvantage of being physically impossible.

FIELD WITHIN A HOLLOW CHARGED SPHERE. Coulomb's law is quite difficult to substantiate experimentally with a high degree of accuracy, because the force that must be measured is small. The best verification of the law is based on the experimental evidence that the force on a charged exploring particle inside a hollow charged sphere is everywhere exactly zero. This measurement, made by Cavendish even before Coulomb's direct measurements of force, and repeated with greater accuracy by Maxwell in the latter half of the nineteenth century, is an experimental proof of the inverse square law, for if electric force from a point charge followed any other law, there would be a resultant force either toward or away from the walls of a hollow charged sphere. This can be proved by integrating to obtain the resultant force exerted on an exploring particle by charge distributed uniformly over the surface of the sphere.

In following the line of argument that has been developed in the preceding chapters, however, the conclusion that there is no electric field within a hollow conducting surface of any shape may be reached from Laplace's equation. Consider any closed conducting surface surrounding empty space. The surface, being conducting, must be equipotential. If any flux lines extend from the surface into the interior space they must be normal to the surface. No flux lines can extend into the interior space and terminate there, for if they did there would be divergence in empty space, and this is inconsistent with Laplace's equation. No flux lines can start from an equipotential surface and return to that same surface; if they did there would be curl in the field, and this is not permitted by Laplace's equation. Therefore no flux lines can enter the interior space from the conducting surface, and there can be no electrostatic field in a cavity (that contains no charge) within a closed conducting surface.

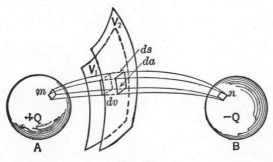

FIG. 28

ELECTROSTATIC ENERGY. A certain amount of energy must be expended to produce an electrostatic field. An exactly equal amount of energy is released when the electrostatic field ceases to exist. While the electrostatic field exists this energy is stored in the field (or, at least, this is the customary assumption). It is even possible to determine the distribution of this energy in the field.

Consider two conducting bodies of any shape, such as A and B of Fig. 28. At first they are uncharged, but electric charge is gradually removed from B and added to A. Because of electrostatic force, a certain amount of work must be done in transferring charge from one body to the other. Since energy is the line integral of force, and potential is the line integral of electric field, it follows from equation 2 that the incremental energy required to transfer a small charge dQ through a potential difference V between the bodies is

$$\text{Incremental energy} = V\,dQ \qquad [115]$$

But V can be expressed in terms of the capacitance of the bodies and of the charge that has already been placed on A before the small charge dQ is transferred, giving

$$\text{Incremental energy} = \frac{Q}{C}\,dQ \qquad [116]$$

The total energy expended in placing a total charge Q upon the bodies is the summation of the small amounts of energy required by the small increments of charge, so the total

$$\text{Energy} = \int_0^Q \frac{Q}{C}\,dQ = \frac{Q^2}{2C} \qquad [117]$$

Since C is, by definition, Q/V, this may be written

$$\text{Energy} = \tfrac{1}{2}QV \qquad [118]$$

The total energy of the system is therefore one-half the product of *the charge on one of the bodies* and *the potential difference between the bodies.* The total energy can be subdivided to determine its distribution in space.

First, the energy corresponding to a given amount of charge is proportional, as in equation 118, to the potential difference through which the charge is moved. Let V_1 and V_2 be the potentials of equipotential surfaces enclosing the body A. A part of each of these surfaces is shown in Fig. 28. These could be actual thin metallic surfaces without altering the electric field. The charge $+Q$ might then be moved from the body A to the surface with potential V_1 (which completely encloses A) and the electric field between A and V_1 would then cease to exist. The electric field between the surface at V_1 and the body B, however, would be unchanged. The surface at V_1 would still be, as before, an equipotential surface; the same amount of flux would issue from it, and would have the same distribution. Now let the charge be moved to the other equipotential surface V_2; the field from V_2 to B will remain unchanged, but the field from V_1 to V_2 will be eliminated. At the same time the energy of the system will be reduced from $\tfrac{1}{2}QV_1$ to $\tfrac{1}{2}QV_2$ (V_1 and V_2 being the potentials of the respective surfaces relative to B). Hence it is reasonable to say that the energy stored in the space between those surfaces was

$$\tfrac{1}{2}Q(V_1 - V_2) \qquad [119]$$

This discussion may be extended to show a division of energy in shells between equipotential surfaces throughout the entire electrostatic field.

Second, the energy of the field may be distributed among the flux lines. If each one-hundredth of the charge on A is responsible for one-hundredth of the energy of the system (which is reasonable from equation 118) and since there issues from that part of the charge one-hundredth of the flux, we may say that this proportion of the energy is located in the space through which the corresponding flux lines pass. In Fig. 28 a tubular section of the space between the charged bodies is indicated as containing flux passing from the small area m on A to n on B. The energy in the tube of space from m to n is proportional to the number of flux lines traversing this tube.

If the tube from m to n is so slim that its cross-section area where it intersects the equipotential surface V_2 is da, and the electric flux density at this cross section is D, the amount of flux in the tube is $D\,da$. The energy in the whole tube is then, from equation 118,

$$\frac{1}{2}\frac{D\,da}{4\pi}V_{AB} \tag{120}$$

If this tube of differential cross-section area is now cut by equipotential surfaces V_1 and V_2 the energy in the tube between those surfaces is, by equations 119 and 120,

$$\frac{1}{2}\frac{D\,da}{4\pi}(V_1 - V_2)$$

Finally, if the spacing between equipotential surfaces is reduced to the differential distance ds, through which the potential drop $V_1 - V_2 = E\,ds$, the energy in the differential volume of space dv is

$$\frac{1}{2}\frac{D\,da}{4\pi}E\,ds = \frac{\kappa}{8\pi}E^2\,dv \tag{121}$$

Energy in any given region of space is obtained by integrating through that region:

$$\text{Energy} = \frac{\kappa}{8\pi}\int E^2\,dv \tag{122}$$

Energy in the entire electric field is found by integrating through infinite space.

That this infinite integral does, indeed, equal the total energy given by equation 118 can be proved directly. But it must not be overlooked that there is no definite proof that the energy *is* stored in space as suggested by equation 121 — we can only say that it behaves as it would *if it were* so stored. The distinction is fundamental and is related to the great controversy between "field theory" and "theory of action at a distance" that raged during the nineteenth century. More will be said of this controversy in a later chapter.

PROBLEMS

1. A charge Q is placed upon an isolated metal sphere of radius r_0. Find electric field strength and potential at all points within the sphere.

2. Two parallel conducting plane surfaces form a condenser. Solve Laplace's equation for the electric field between the surfaces when they have charge ω and $-\omega$ per unit area. Find capacitance per unit area. (Consider a region that is so far from the edges of the surfaces that the electric charge is uniformly distributed.)

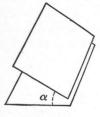

PROB. 3

3. Find the electric field between two charged plane conducting surfaces set at an angle α, but not quite touching. Find the distribution of charge on the surfaces. Consider, as in Problem 2, a region distant from the edges, so that the result is not influenced by edge effects.

4. Find the electric field about an isolated cylindrical conductor of radius r_0 and unlimited length with a charge of q units per unit length. Find the curl of this electric field.

5. Find the potential difference between the conductor of Problem 4 and any point in space.

6. Find a law (similar to the inverse square law for charged spheres) to be used for force between charged parallel cylinders of unlimited length.

7. Find the energy required to charge unit area of the condenser of Problem 2, using equation 118. Find the energy in the electrostatic field of that condenser, per unit volume, using equation 122.

8. Using equations 1 and 4 (instead of 2 and 5) find the general form of Coulomb's law that applies in any system of units.

9. Two parallel metal plates are close together but insulated. They are charged, one being positive and the other negative. They are connected by flexible wires to an electroscope. Without permitting any change in the charge on either plate the plates are separated. Explain why the electroscope indicates a greatly increased voltage between plates as the plates are drawn apart. If the initial separation is 0.1 millimeter and the initial voltage difference 100 volts, find the voltage between them when they are separated 10 centimeters. (Note: This explains the high voltages of lightning.)

10. Find the capacitance per square centimeter of a pair of large parallel plates 1 centimeter apart in air. Convert the result to micromicrofarads (10^{-12} farads). Remember this result, at least approximately, for it is often useful in estimating capacitances.

Chapter V

DIELECTRIC MATERIALS

There are two ways of thinking of the behavior of dielectric materials. One is analogous to familiar ideas of magnetism and electric current, and is easy to understand and apply. The other, although nearly as simple in its essential idea, is less familiar, but is believed to be an approximation of physical reality.

The first concept pictures electric field strength **E** as a driving force and electric flux density **D** as the effect.[1] They are analogous to voltage and current in an electric circuit. Some materials (those with high dielectric constant) are then looked upon as permitting more flux for a given electric field strength, an effect analogous to high conductivity.

E and **D** are also analogous to the magnetic quantities **H** and **B**, magnetic field strength and magnetic flux density, and κ is analogous to the magnetic permeability μ.

This concept of electrostatic behavior is adequate for most purposes, and seems usually to be the most convenient for a mental picture of fields and their distribution. Flux lines extend from positive charge to negative charge, following the path of highest dielectric constant in as far as possible, yet spreading out like Faraday's " mutually repulsive rubber bands." The driving force for the flux is the electric field, less field strength being needed for a given amount of flux in a substance of high dielectric constant.

Force. Force on an exploring particle is proportional to the electric field strength **E**, as in equation 2.

The force between two charged bodies is less in dielectric material than in free space. Consider a charged body submerged in oil with a dielectric constant κ. The same number of flux lines emanate from the charged body as in free space (4π times the charge) and if oil extends indefinitely in all directions the flux pattern is the same as in free space, for it must satisfy Laplace's equation. Hence the vector field of flux density **D** is the same as in free space. But in oil the electric field strength **E** is less than the flux density **D** by the factor κ, and hence, by equation 2, the force on a charged body in the field is less by the

---

[1] Gaussian units of these quantities have only derived names, **E** being in statvolts per centimeter and **D** in electrostatic flux lines per square centimeter.

same factor. (This, indeed, instead of Experiment IV, might have been taken as the experimental basis for deductions concerning the electric field in material substance, but the mathematics would have been less simple.)

CAPACITANCE. The capacitance of any condenser is increased by placing dielectric material between the condenser surfaces. Consider the spherical condenser of Fig. 27 with the space between the spherical surfaces A and B filled with sulphur with dielectric constant κ. A charge Q is placed upon the condenser ($+Q$ on the inner sphere, $-Q$ on the outer). The electrostatic field is radial and, as in equation 106,

$$E = \frac{D}{\kappa} = \frac{Q}{\kappa\, r^2} \tag{123}$$

The condenser voltage will then be, as in equation 109,

$$V_{AB} = \int_a^b E\, dr = \frac{Q(b - a)}{\kappa\, ab} \tag{124}$$

Finally, the capacitance is

$$C = \frac{Q}{V} = \kappa\, \frac{ab}{b - a} \tag{125}$$

and this is greater than the capacitance of the same condenser in free space by the factor κ. (This fact also might have been taken as the experimental basis for discussion of dielectric materials. Indeed, it is the method that was actually used in the classical determination of the properties of dielectric substances by Faraday and others. It is the most satisfactory experimental approach, but mathematical relations of general applicability are not easily derived from it.)

POLARIZATION. The alternative concept of the behavior of dielectric materials assumes **polarization** of the material. It is supposed that all non-conducting material contains positive and negative charges bound together, perhaps by being part of the same atom. When material of this kind is in an electric field the positive charges tend to move one way and the negative charges the other, but since they are bound they can move only as far as the elastic nature of the bond permits. Each atom is somewhat distorted, therefore, by the stress of the electric field and becomes positive on one side and negative on the other.

Figure 29 shows a block of dielectric material between a pair of charged metal plates, one with charge $+Q$ and the other with $-Q$. In the upper part of the diagram the material is shown so much enlarged that the elementary particles can be seen; they are strained by the electric field so that each is negative on the left and positive on the right. The result is that the left-hand surface of the material is predominantly negative and the right-hand surface positive. Any cubic centimeter of the material, however, contains equal numbers of positive and negative elements and is neutral.

In this way, without any flow of free charge through the material, but merely as a result of polarization, the material has acquired the equivalent of a surface charge. Flux lines, according to this theory, terminate on the charge of polarization on the dielectric surface, as shown in the lower part of Fig. 29. It is apparent that in such a case the electric field within the dielectric material will be less than in the space on either side.

The amount of polarization of dielectric material is proportional to

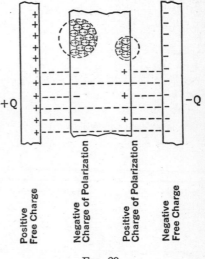

FIG. 29

the electric field strength in the material, and the surface charge per unit area resulting from polarization is proportional to the normal component of electric field at the surface. A high susceptibility to polarization in this theory corresponds to a high dielectric constant in the other theory.

In the theory of polarization $D = \kappa E$ is merely a mathematical fiction, convenient in computation but not corresponding to any physical reality in a dielectric material. "Dielectric constant" is no part of this theory. Instead of picturing a dielectric material as one in which the electric field strength may be small even though the flux density is great, it is understood that in a dielectric material the electric field strength is small because the flux density is small also. Referring again to Fig. 29, many flux lines fail to penetrate into the dielectric material because they terminate on surface charge of polarization. Electric field strength is less in a dielectric material than in free space, as in Fig. 29, not because of some inherent but unexplained property of the material, but because the space within the dielectric material is partially shielded by surface charges.

To summarize:

THEORY OF DIELECTRIC CONSTANT	THEORY OF POLARIZATION
E and **D** are related by κ, a characteristic of the material.	**E** is the electric field; **D** is not part of this theory.
Only free charge is considered, and **D** has no divergence except at free charge.	Both free charge and charge of polarization must be considered, the susceptibility to polarization being a characteristic of the material.
Polarization is not part of this theory.	Dielectric constant is not part of this theory.
This concept is better adapted to most practical computations.	This concept is more satisfactory for theoretical purposes.

PROBLEMS

1. Find from handbooks or other sources the dielectric constants of the following materials. If there is any choice, select values at normal temperature and pressure.

SOLIDS	LIQUIDS	GASES
Bakelite	Alcohol, methyl	Air
Diamond	ethyl	Carbon dioxide
Glass, soft	Oil (petroleum	Water vapor
hard	derivative)	
flint	Water	
Ice		
Mica		
Paraffin		
Porcelain		
Quartz		
Rubber		
Sulphur		

2. Find the capacitance of a spherical condenser as in Fig. 27 if the space surrounding the inner sphere A is filled with paraffin out to a radius equal to $\frac{1}{2}(a + b)$. Find the electric field in both paraffin and empty space that results from a charge Q on the condenser.

3. Referring to Problem 9 of Chapter IV: if the initial separation is 0.1 millimeter of *paraffined paper* with a dielectric constant of 2.3, find the voltage when the plates are separated by 10 centimeters of air.

CHAPTER VI

ELECTRIC CURRENT

In electrostatic problems, materials are divided into two classes: conductors and non-conductors. Electrostatics is not concerned with the relative ability of different conducting materials to permit charge to flow, for if there is any motion of charge the condition is not electrostatic.

If an electric field exists in a conducting material, electric charge in the material will be driven to flow in the general direction of the electric field. Such flow of charge is called an **electric current;** the electric current through any given surface is equal, by definition, to the rate of flow of electric charge past that surface. That is,

$$I = \frac{dQ}{dt} \qquad [126]$$

in which Q is the total charge that has passed through the surface.

An experiment is now necessary to determine the current-carrying characteristics of various conducting materials. This experiment, which will be called Experiment V, is actually the work of Georg Ohm, and the result is **Ohm's law.**

EXPERIMENT V. Current flowing in a metallic conductor is measured, and the voltage difference is determined between the ends of a section of the conductor (each end of the section is an equipotential surface). The voltage is maintained constant while performing the experiment. This is done for an unlimited variety of sizes and shapes of conductors, and for many different metallic materials. It is found that the current and voltage are always related by

$$I = \frac{1}{R} V \qquad [127]$$

where R is a constant determined by the composition and geometry of the conductor.[1] It is found, moreover, that R is directly proportional

---

[1] Temperature and other physical conditions affect R to some extent. The essential point is that a given sample of material has a certain resistance which is a characteristic of the material and is not dependent upon the amount of current flowing or the voltage applied.

to the length of a conductor of constant cross section, and inversely proportional to the cross section of a conductor of constant length, so with γ as a coefficient that is characteristic of the conductor material

$$\frac{1}{R} = \gamma \frac{\text{area}}{\text{length}} \tag{128}$$

The coefficient γ is called the **conductivity** of the material.

Voltage was defined by equation 108 as the integral of electric field strength:

$$V = \int \mathbf{E} \cdot d\mathbf{s} \tag{129}$$

It is now desirable to introduce a new term, **current density, ι,** which is so defined that the integral of it over a surface gives the current through that surface:

$$I = \int \iota \cdot d\mathbf{a} \tag{130}$$

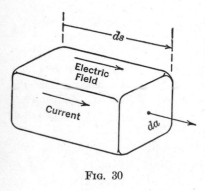

Fig. 30

Since Ohm's law applies to all shapes and sizes of conductors, it applies to a section of differentially small size. Consider the section shown in Fig. 30. The current flowing through this section is $\iota \cdot d\mathbf{a}$ (from equation 130) and the voltage from end to end is $\mathbf{E} \cdot d\mathbf{s}$ (from equation 129) and

$$\frac{1}{R} = \gamma \frac{da}{ds} \tag{131}$$

from equation 128. Combining these in Ohm's law, equation 127,

$$\iota \cdot d\mathbf{a} = \gamma \frac{da}{ds} \mathbf{E} \cdot d\mathbf{s} \tag{132}$$

Since $d\mathbf{s}$ and $d\mathbf{a}$, considered as vectors, have the same direction as $\mathbf{E}$ and ι, current density and electric field strength are related simply as

$$\iota = \gamma \mathbf{E} \tag{133}$$

This resulting equation is a *microscopic* Ohm's law. It says that the current density at any point in a conductor is proportional to the electric field strength at that point, and in the same direction. This is true for metallic conductors, to which the above discussion has been limited.

It is true for electrolytic conductors, also, and for many other conducting materials. (But it is not true for certain crystalline substances, such as carborundum, in which current is not proportional to voltage, nor to anisotropic material in which conductivity is not the same in different directions, nor to the passage of electricity through gases; Ohm's law does not apply to these cases without special interpretation. Cases in which equation 133 does not apply will not be considered further.)

When the electric field is not varying (as was specified in Experiment V) there can be no change of accumulated charge, for, if there were a change of charge, there would be a change of electric field also. It follows that whatever electrostatic charge there may be on the surface of the conductor will remain there, unchanged, while current flows through the cross section of the conductor. To repeat, since there is no change of electric field there is no change of charge density at any point. Since there is no change of charge density at any point the lines of current flow do not terminate. Since the lines of current flow do not terminate, the vector field of current density has no divergence. That is,

$$\nabla \cdot \iota = 0 \qquad [134]$$

or, from equation 133, within the conductor,

$$\nabla \cdot \gamma \, E = \gamma \nabla \cdot E = 0 \qquad [135]$$

when the flow of current is steady and the electric field is unchanging.

Kirchhoff's first law may be stated: The algebraic sum of the currents flowing toward a junction in an electrical network is zero. This is clearly a special case of the more general relation of equation 134, and may be considered to be derived from it.

If, as a result of current flowing, charge is accumulating in some part of the circuit, equations 134 and 135 do not apply. Consider, for instance, the parallel-plate condenser of Fig. 31. Current is flowing into the left-hand plate, and from the right-hand plate. No current, however, is flowing in the space between the plates, but the electric field **E** in that region is constantly increasing as charge is deposited on one plate of the condenser and removed from the other.

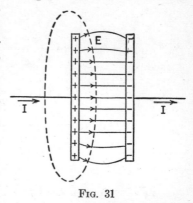

Fig. 31

Now imagine a closed surface about one of the plates, as indicated by the dash line. Charge is entering this closed surface, because of the current I, but no charge is leaving it. Consequently the amount of charge within the surface is increasing, and therefore the amount of electric flux passing out through the surface is increasing.

The rate of increase of charge within the surface is I, for by equation 126, $I = dQ/dt$. Since 4π lines of flux emanate from each unit of charge, the rate of increase of flux passing through the surface is

$$\frac{d}{dt}(\text{flux}) = 4\pi \frac{d}{dt} Q = 4\pi I \qquad [136]$$

However,

$$\text{Flux} = \int \mathbf{D} \cdot d\mathbf{a} \qquad [137]$$

so the current entering any closed surface is related to the flux passing out through that surface by

$$I = \frac{1}{4\pi} \frac{d}{dt} \oint \mathbf{D} \cdot d\mathbf{a} = \frac{1}{4\pi} \oint \frac{d\mathbf{D}}{dt} \cdot d\mathbf{a} \qquad [138]$$

The current flowing out through a closed surface is found by integrating current density over that surface:

$$\oint \iota \cdot d\mathbf{a} \qquad [139]$$

and since equation 138 is for current *entering*, we may equate

$$-\oint \iota \cdot d\mathbf{a} = \frac{1}{4\pi} \oint \frac{d\mathbf{D}}{dt} \cdot d\mathbf{a} \qquad [140]$$

The two integrations of equation 140 are performed over the same closed surface, so

$$\oint \left(\iota + \frac{1}{4\pi} \frac{d\mathbf{D}}{dt} \right) \cdot d\mathbf{a} = 0 \qquad [141]$$

whence, by Gauss's theorem

$$\int \nabla \cdot \left(\iota + \frac{1}{4\pi} \frac{d\mathbf{D}}{dt} \right) dv = 0 \qquad [142]$$

and since this is true for the space contained within any closed surface, however large or small, it follows that everywhere the quantity in parentheses has zero divergence:

$$\nabla \cdot \left(\iota + \frac{1}{4\pi} \frac{d\mathbf{D}}{dt} \right) = 0 \qquad [143]$$

Two obvious substitutions in equation 143 then give

$$\nabla \cdot \left(\gamma \mathbf{E} + \frac{\kappa}{4\pi} \frac{d\mathbf{E}}{dt} \right) = 0 \qquad [144]$$

Comparison of equation 143 with 134 is very enlightening. Equation 134 tells us that current has no divergence in steady flow, that is, if the electric field strength is unchanging. If the electric field is changing, however, current does not flow without divergence. But, as we are informed by equation 143, if another term involving the rate of change of the electric field is added to current density at every point, the result is a quantity that has zero divergence under all circumstances.

We are tempted to look upon this additional quantity, this $\frac{\kappa}{4\pi} \frac{d\mathbf{E}}{dt}$, as something similar to current — perhaps even as a kind of current itself. It is not a **conduction current**, which is the name given to $\gamma \mathbf{E}$, so we will call it a **displacement current**. The total current, the sum of conduction current and displacement current, according to this terminology, is made up of two parts:

$$\iota_t = \iota_c + \iota_d = \gamma \mathbf{E} + \frac{\kappa}{4\pi} \frac{d\mathbf{E}}{dt} \qquad [145]$$

The divergence of this *total* current density is always zero, and ι_t is therefore *solenoidal*.

ELECTROMOTIVE FORCE. When current flows in conducting material there is a certain amount of energy loss. The energy lost in this manner must be provided from some source, and may come from the chemical action of a battery, or from thermal action, or (as will be seen in Chapter VII) from magnetic action, or it may have its source in certain other phenomena. In any case the source of energy provides what is known as an **electromotive force**.

Voltage, as that term is commonly used, is a measure of the tendency of current to flow, and as in Ohm's law

$$V = IR \qquad [146]$$

Voltage is made up of two parts. First, current may flow as a result of the electric field between electrically charged bodies. It is this kind of driving force that causes current to flow through a wire that is connected from one to another of a pair of charged conducting surfaces, as in a condenser. This component of voltage might be called the electrostatic driving force (except that when current flows the condition is not electrostatic) and it will be designated V_s.

Second, current may also flow as a result of there being a battery or a thermocouple or a generator in the circuit, exerting an electromotive force which will be represented by V_m. In general, as in a circuit with both a battery and a condenser, both V_s and V_m will exist and the total voltage will be the sum

$$V = V_s + V_m = IR \qquad [147]$$

This is Ohm's law, with the significance of the voltage V extended to include electromotive force.

In any part of the circuit in which electromotive forces are not operating, only V_s exists, and there

$$V = V_s = \int \mathbf{E}_s \cdot d\mathbf{s} = IR \qquad [148]$$

as in equation 129. If there is also electromotive force present, V_m must be added. If the electromotive force is distributed along the conductor (as is a magnetically induced electromotive force) V_m is the line integral, along the conductor, of the induced electric field $\mathbf{E}_m$, which exists at each point along the conductor. Thus in general

$$V = V_s + V_m = \int \mathbf{E}_s \cdot d\mathbf{s} + \int \mathbf{E}_m \cdot d\mathbf{s} = IR \qquad [149]$$

the integration being performed along a path within the conductor.

Microscopically, the electric field within a conductor is made up of two parts: the part $\mathbf{E}_s$ which results from the presence of electric charge and which corresponds to the electrostatic field, and the part $\mathbf{E}_m$ which is induced by magnetic (or chemical or thermal) action. The total electric field in the conductor is the sum of these:

$$\mathbf{E} = \mathbf{E}_s + \mathbf{E}_m \qquad [150]$$

and the current density is found from equation 133 to be

$$\iota = \gamma \mathbf{E} = \gamma(\mathbf{E}_s + \mathbf{E}_m) \qquad [151]$$

If circumstances are such that there is no current in a conductor, it must either be that $\mathbf{E}_s$ and $\mathbf{E}_m$ are both zero, or else that the electrostatic field and the induced electromotive field are exactly equal and opposite at every point.

A particularly interesting special case of equation 149 is found in a closed circuit containing an electromotive force. When the path of integration of equation 149 is a closed path following the circuit we have

$$\oint \mathbf{E}_s \cdot d\mathbf{s} + \oint \mathbf{E}_m \cdot d\mathbf{s} = IR \qquad [152]$$

But the integral of $\mathbf{E}_s$ around a *closed* path is necessarily zero, as in all electrostatic fields, and consequently

$$IR = \oint \mathbf{E}_m \cdot d\mathbf{s} = \text{Electromotive force} \qquad [153]$$

This relation will be of use in the next chapter, in exploring the magnetic field.

PROBLEMS

1. Find, from tables or otherwise, the conductivity of copper, iron, and aluminum. Give values in electrostatic units.

2. Derive Kirchhoff's first law, as stated on page 69, from equation 134. Kirchhoff's second law says, in effect, that in the absence of electromotive forces the sum of the voltages around any circuit of a network is zero; derive this law, also, as a special case of an equation in Chapter IV.

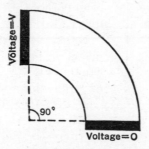

PROB. 3

3. A flat metal plate of uniform thickness is bounded by two quarter-circles and two radial lines, as shown in the figure. A constant direct voltage is maintained at the edges bounded by radial lines. Find the distribution of current density in the plate.

4. Thickness of the plate of Problem 3 is $\frac{1}{16}$ inch, the inner edge has 1-inch and the outer edge 2-inch radius of curvature. Total current is 100 amperes. Find the maximum current density in the plate.

5. The material of the plate of Problems 3 and 4 is aluminum: Find the maximum rate of production of heat per unit volume under the above conditions.

CHAPTER VII

THE MAGNETIC FIELD

MAGNETIC FORCE. When a conductor is carrying current there may be a mechanical force exerted upon it. This is quite distinct from electrostatic force and from all non-electrical forces, for it disappears when current ceases to flow. This force is observed when the conductor is in the neighborhood of another conductor that is also carrying current or when it is in the neighborhood of a magnet. It is therefore called magnetic force.

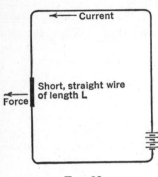

FIG. 32

EXPERIMENT VI is performed to study magnetic force. The apparatus is indicated in Fig. 32. A short, straight section of conducting wire is mounted in such a way that force exerted upon it can be measured while current is flowing through it from end to end. Since the short section of wire must be free to move, in order to measure force, some kind of flexible connection is used to carry current to it. An arrangement of pools of mercury might well be employed.[1]

The experiment shows that magnetic force on the exploring wire is always normal to the wire. The amount of the force is proportional to the amount of current flowing through the wire. The force is also proportional to the length of the exploring section of wire. All these factors are easily understood, for they depend upon the exploring wire and the current in the exploring wire. But the amount and direction of the magnetic force are also dependent upon the location and the orientation of the exploring wire in space, particularly with reference to magnets and to other circuits carrying electric current. This suggests that there is some condition in space (especially in the space about magnets and electric currents) which produces the magnetic force. It suggests that we would do well to consider the possible existence of a **magnetic field.**

The experimental evidence tells us that at any point in space it is possible to orient the exploring wire in such a way that there is no

---

[1] Historically, various forms of this apparatus were used by Ampère in 1821 in establishing the law of force between conductors that is known as " Ampère's law."

magnetic force upon it.   If the exploring wire is held at the same point, but turned to a new orientation, there is then a magnetic force; and the amount of the force is proportional to the sine of the angle between the direction of the exploring wire and its direction when the force is zero. The magnetic force reaches a maximum when the wire is perpendicular to its null direction.   The direction of the magnetic force, in addition to being normal to the wire, is also normal to the null direction.

From these experimental results it is seen that the idea of a magnetic field is quite reasonable.   It must be a vector field with direction as well as magnitude.   There is only one uniquely defined direction: the direction of the exploring wire when the magnetic force upon it is zero. This is taken, by definition, to be the *direction* of the magnetic field. The *strength* of the magnetic field is found from the maximum magnetic force that appears when the exploring wire is normal to the null position; the magnetic field strength is defined as proportional to this maximum force.   The *sense* of the field is also defined in terms of this maximum force, for a "right-hand" relation is assumed between the positive direction of current flow in the exploring wire, positive direction of magnetic field, and the sense of the resultant force.

With these definitions we are able to compute the magnetic force upon the exploring wire from the following equation:

$$\mathbf{F} = \frac{I\mathbf{L} {\times} \mathbf{B}}{c} \qquad [154]$$

The force is represented by $\mathbf{F}$, $\mathbf{L}$ is the length of the section of exploring wire on which the force is exerted, and I is the current that it carries. $\mathbf{B}$ is called the **magnetic induction** (as will be seen later, it is also the **magnetic flux density**), and c is a factor of proportionality.   The value of c depends upon the units used; in the Gaussian system c is almost exactly 3×10^{10}, whereas in the electromagnetic system it is unity by definition.   It will be noticed that the current is written as a scalar quantity, while $\mathbf{L}$, the length of the wire that carries the current, is a vector, and its direction is obviously the direction of the wire.   The positive sense of $\mathbf{L}$ is arbitrarily selected, and when current flows in the positive direction it is positive current.   (It is possible in equation 154 to write current as a vector and length as a scalar quantity; but in other cases it is often impossible to consider current as a vector quantity, and indeed it is defined as scalar in Chapter VI.)

Equation 154 takes into account all the facts discovered by Experiment VI.   It would be well for the reader to review the experimental results as described above, and to see how they are incorporated in the equation.

MAGNETIC FLUX. Lines of **magnetic flux** may be conceived just as were lines of electrostatic flux, and the definition is similar.

$$\text{Magnetic flux} = \Phi = \int \mathbf{B} \cdot d\mathbf{a} \qquad [155]$$

The quantity **B** is magnetic flux density, for when multiplied by an area (or integrated over an area, as in equation 155) the product is flux. The unit of flux is the *maxwell*, and the unit of flux density, which is one maxwell per square centimeter, is called the *gauss*.

EXPERIMENT VII. Another experiment will now be performed to study the relation between the magnetic and the electric fields. The discovery that an electric field could be produced magnetically was made by Michael Faraday in England in 1831, and it is often considered to be the most significant of his many valuable experiments. It was made independently, but a few months later, by Joseph Henry in the United States.

The apparatus for Experiment VII is a loop of wire connected to a ballistic galvanometer. The arrangement of the apparatus may be as

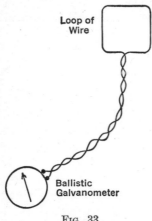

Loop of Wire

Ballistic Galvanometer

FIG. 33

in Fig. 33 in which a twisted pair of wires is indicated between the loop and the galvanometer. The reading of a ballistic galvanometer is a measure of the electric charge that passes through it, and it is found that if the loop is in a magnetic field the galvanometer indicates that charge flows whenever the magnetic field strength is increased or decreased. We measure the magnetic flux density at the loop by the methods of Experiment VI, and find that the reading of the ballistic galvanometer is proportional to the increase or decrease of flux passing through the loop of our apparatus. It is also determined that deflection of the galvanometer is inversely proportional to the total resistance of the apparatus including loop, leads, and galvanometer. Since the galvanometer measures electric charge we write

$$Q = -\frac{\Phi}{cR} \qquad [156]$$

As in equation 154, c is a factor of proportionality very nearly equal to 3×10^{10}. The negative sign in equation 156 indicates that if the positive direction of flow of charge around the loop is related to the direction of positive flux by the " right-hand rule," a positive increase of flux produces a negative current.

From equation 156, Faraday's law of induction is deduced. The equation can be written

$$RQ = -\frac{\Phi}{c} \qquad [157]$$

and by differentiation

$$R \frac{\partial Q}{\partial t} = RI = -\frac{1}{c} \frac{\partial \Phi}{\partial t} \qquad [158]$$

It was shown in Chapter VI that in a closed circuit the product RI is equal to electromotive force around the circuit, so from equations 153 and 158

$$\text{Electromotic force} = \oint \mathbf{E} \cdot d\mathbf{s} = -\frac{1}{c} \frac{\partial \Phi}{\partial t} \qquad [159]$$

This is Faraday's famous law. It is, of course, in Gaussian units, and the flux Φ is that which passes through a surface bounded by the conductor and corresponds to the usual concept of flux linkages (see page 87).

Magnetically induced electromotive force around a loop of wire is given by Equation 159, and it is expressed as the line integral of the electric field along the conducting loop. A generalization of this experimental relation will now be made: It will be assumed that a changing magnetic field induces an electric field according to equation 159 not only in conducting material but also in non-conducting material, and even in empty space. This is reasonable, for if the loop of copper wire of Experiment VII is replaced by a loop of poorly conducting material such as a nickel-chromium alloy the induced voltage in the loop remains exactly the same. Voltage is induced even in a piece of wood in a changing magnetic field, and if the current that flows is very small it is merely because the resistivity of the wood is quite high. This fact can be established experimentally, if suitably delicate instruments are available, and it is not a difficult step to assume that if this is true in all materials it is true in air or even in empty space. At first sight this would appear to be a mere quibble, for what does it matter whether an electric field is produced if there is no material present for it to act upon? But it will be seen a little later that this concept is in reality of the utmost importance, and that without electric and magnetic fields producing each other in free space there could be no transmission of radio, light, or other electromagnetic waves through vacuum.

With this assumption (which establishes that there is an induced electric field that is continuous in space) Stokes' theorem can be applied to the integral of equation 159. At the same time expression 155 may be substituted for flux, giving

$$\int (\nabla \times \mathbf{E}) \cdot d\mathbf{a} = -\frac{1}{c} \int \frac{\partial \mathbf{B}}{\partial t} \cdot d\mathbf{a} \qquad [160]$$

These two integrations are both over a surface bounded by the conductor of the experimental apparatus, which may be of any size, shape, or orientation, and the two sides of the equation can be equal under all circumstances only if

$$\nabla \times \mathbf{E} = -\frac{1}{c} \frac{\partial \mathbf{B}}{\partial t} \qquad [161]$$

This equation shows that an electric field will have curl in a region in which the magnetic field is changing with time. The electro*static* field, it will be remembered, in which nothing changes with time, has no curl. The great importance of this equation will appear in Chapter IX.

VOLTAGE INDUCED BY MOTION. In deriving the right-hand member of equation 160 from equation 159 it is assumed that flux through a loop changes only because the magnetic flux density is changing. But it is also possible for the loop to be traveling through space, as, for example, in an electric generator, and its motion through the magnetic field may then alter the amount of flux that passes through the loop even though the strength of the magnetic field at every fixed point of space is constant. In general,[2] if a medium is moving with velocity **v** through space in which the magnetic field is **B** there will be an electric field induced in the medium, as a result of its motion, equal to **v**×**B**. This is in addition to any electric field that results from a changing magnetic field strength, and when it is considered equation 161 (which is valid for media at rest) becomes (for moving media)

$$\nabla \times \mathbf{E} = -\frac{1}{c} \left[\frac{\partial \mathbf{B}}{\partial t} - \nabla \times (\mathbf{v} \times \mathbf{B}) \right] \qquad [162]$$

EXPERIMENT VIII. A magnetic field has been defined in terms of the force exerted on a wire carrying current. It has also been seen that a changing magnetic field induces an electric field. But neither the source of the magnetic field nor its configuration in space has yet been

---

[2] See a more advanced treatise on electromagnetic theory, such as *Classical Electricity and Magnetism*, by Abraham and Becker, G. E. Stechert & Co., New York.

considered. More experimental information is required for this purpose, and two more experiments will now be described. These are very closely analogous to Experiments II and III that were performed in studying electric fields. It will be seen that both of these experiments in the magnetic field, Experiments VIII and IX, can be done only in a magnetic field that is not changing with time; such a field, by analogy to the electrostatic field, is called *magnetostatic*.

Experiment VIII is performed with an instrument for measuring magnetic flux density. It may be either the current-carrying wire that was used in Experiment VI or the loop and ballistic galvanometer of Experiment VII. The latter would be the more practical. Indeed an exploring loop, usually of many turns wound tightly together, connected by flexible leads to a properly calibrated ballistic galvanometer of extremely long natural period, is a common laboratory instrument known as a " fluxmeter."

The instrument for measuring magnetic flux density is used to determine the normal component of the quantity **B** at all points on a closed surface in a magnetic field. The closed surface is merely an imaginary one, and it may have any shape or size. This experiment must be repeated for very many such surfaces, and the conclusion from the experimental data is that in all cases the summation of the magnetic field over every closed surface is zero. That is,

$$\oint \mathbf{B} \cdot d\mathbf{a} = 0 \qquad [163]$$

Applying Gauss's theorem to this experimental result, it appears that the magnetic field has no divergence under any circumstances:

$$\nabla \cdot \mathbf{B} = 0 \qquad [164]$$

Lines of magnetic flux are therefore continuous, for it follows from equation 164 that no magnetic flux line has a beginning or end. Every one is a closed loop.

Experiment VIII is performed in material substance of all kinds, as well as in free space, and the result is the same: divergence of the magnetic field is always zero. It is obviously impossible to explore the magnetic field within a solid substance such as brass or iron by measuring force on a conductor, but the fluxmeter loop can be used to determine the total magnetic flux within any piece of solid material, and the result is found to be always consistent with equation 164.

EXPERIMENT IX. This, the last of our experiments, may be done with either of the instruments suggested for Experiment VIII. As before, however, the exploring loop of a fluxmeter is the only way to determine the amount of magnetic flux within solid material. The measuring instrument is used in Experiment IX to determine the magnetic flux density at every point of a closed path, and by summing the tangential component of the magnetic flux density along the chosen path the integral

$$\oint \mathbf{B} \cdot d\mathbf{s}$$

is evaluated.

It is first discovered that if the path of integration lies in homogeneous material, the value of the integral is proportional to the amount of electric current surrounded by the path of integration. If no electric current flows through a surface bounded by the path of integration, the value of the integral (in homogeneous material) is zero. If current flows in such a way as to link the path of integration, however, the value of the integral is given by

$$\frac{1}{\mu} \oint \mathbf{B} \cdot d\mathbf{s} = \frac{4\pi}{c} I \qquad [165]$$

The current is I, c is the same constant of proportionality that has been encountered in previous work, and μ is a value that is characteristic of the material. The coefficient μ is called **permeability**; it is unity (in Gaussian units) in free space.

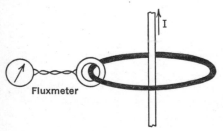

Fluxmeter

Fig. 34

This experiment may be performed on a ring of iron, as in Fig. 34. The exploring loop of the fluxmeter is wrapped around the iron to measure the flux that exists within the metal. A wire is threaded through the ring and is adjusted to pass normally through its center. A known value of current is then allowed to flow in the wire, and the resulting deflection of the ballistic galvanometer is observed. This is repeated with the exploring loop at various places on the ring (although it is found that the galvanometer reading is the same at all locations). The iron ring is then removed, and the experiment is repeated with the exploring loop of the fluxmeter enclosing merely empty space. Since the readings of the fluxmeter when used on the iron ring are some hundreds of times greater than when iron is absent, it follows that the permeability of the iron (under the conditions of the experiment) is several hundred.

Experiment shows that the permeability of most materials is practically unity, as is that of free space. Only iron, cobalt, nickel, and certain alloys have magnetic permeabilities differing from unity by as much as a few parts in a million. These have high permeabilities, ranging up to many thousand, and because iron is typical of the group they are known as **ferromagnetic** materials. They are extremely unsatisfactory for analytical study because their permeability is not constant but depends upon the magnetic flux density (as exemplified in the extreme case by magnetic saturation) and what is worse the permeability is affected by the previous magnetic history of the material (as seen in the phenomena of hysteresis and permanent magnetism). Fortunately it is not often necessary to consider ferromagnetic materials in connection with electric waves. In this chapter it will be assumed that permeability is constant even in those ferromagnetic materials in which it differs significantly from unity.

Finally, when the investigation of Experiment IX is extended to the measurement of magnetic flux density along paths that are partly in one material and partly in another, it is necessary to associate the proper value of permeability with each part of the path. For a path of integration in non-homogeneous material, equation 165 accordingly becomes

$$\oint \frac{\mathbf{B} \cdot d\mathbf{s}}{\mu} = \frac{4\pi}{c} I \qquad [166]$$

By introducing a new symbol, **H**, representing the vector field of **magnetic intensity**, defined in accordance with the relation $\mathbf{B} = \mu\mathbf{H}$, it is possible to write equation 166 as:

$$\oint \mathbf{H} \cdot d\mathbf{s} = \frac{4\pi}{c} I \qquad [167]$$

This equation is found to be true for all possible closed paths of integration, and it sums up the results obtained by performing Experiment IX.

Equation 167 is an equation of **magnetomotive force**. The Gaussian unit of magnetomotive force is the *gilbert*. (The practical unit, the *ampere-turn*, is roughly equivalent to a gilbert, for they are related by the factor $10/4\pi$ [see Table I].)

The current I may be the current in a single conductor, as in Fig. 35a, or in several conductors, as in Fig. 35b, c, or d, or in part of a conductor, as in e. The current may be merely a diffuse flow of charge throughout the entire region, as in f. In any case it may be defined as the integral of the current density over a surface bounded by the path of integration:

$$I = \int \iota \cdot d\mathbf{a} \qquad [168]$$

The surface of integration of equation 168 may be *any* surface bounded
by the closed path, for (under the circumstances of the experiment)

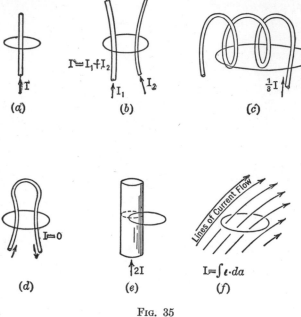

Fig. 35

if a line of current flow links the path of intergation it will pass through
any surface bounded by that path.

Introducing equation 168 into 167 gives

$$\oint \mathbf{H} \cdot d\mathbf{s} = \frac{4\pi}{c} \int \iota \cdot d\mathbf{a} \qquad [169]$$

By means of Stokes' theorem the left-hand member of equation 169
can be changed from a line integral around a closed path to a surface
integral over a surface bounded by that path:

$$\oint \mathbf{H} \cdot d\mathbf{s} = \int (\nabla \times \mathbf{H}) \cdot d\mathbf{a} = \frac{4\pi}{c} \int \iota \cdot d\mathbf{a} \qquad [170]$$

The second and third members of equation 170 can therefore be integrations over the same surface, which may be any surface, and it follows
that at each point

$$\nabla \times \mathbf{H} = \frac{4\pi}{c} \iota \qquad [171]$$

This equation says that the curl of the magnetic field at any point is proportional to the current density at that point. Where there is no current the field has no curl and is therefore lamellar, but in space through which current is flowing the magnetic field has more or less curl. There is curl, for instance, in a magnetic field *within* a wire that is carrying current.

CONVENTION REGARDING SIGN. In equations 165, 166, and 167 the meaning of the algebraic sign is as yet undefined. Equation 167, for example, states that current flowing in a wire produces magnetomotive force along a path encircling that wire. The question must arise: In which way is the magnetomotive force directed? What is meant by a positive current or a positive magnetomotive force?

To clarify this situation a new definition is needed. When direction around a circle is to be related to direction normal to the plane of the circle, one or the other of the possible relations must arbitrarily be accepted as positive. It is customary to assume that if a circle were drawn in the plane of this page, and if the positive direction around the circle were taken to be counterclockwise, the positive normal direction would be out of the page. If, on the other hand, the positive direction around the circle were taken to be clockwise, the positive normal direction would be in. To express this relation in a single word, let us use the term *boreal*.[3] This makes it possible to state quite simply the accepted convention relating circuital and axial directions: the boreal direction is positive.

When a so-called right-hand screw is turned it advances in a direction boreal to its rotation. The thumb of the right hand is boreal to the fingers when held as in Fig. 36c. This establishes the " right-hand rule " which is, indeed, the most convenient way to find the boreal direction in individual cases. As in equation 167, current in a wire is boreal to the magnetomotive force it produces; hence if the right thumb is pointed along the wire in the direction of current flow the fingers indicate the positive magnetomotive force (see Fig. 36b).

In the discussion following equation 156, page 76, the relative directions of induced current in a loop of wire and the flux linking the loop were considered. The statement can now be made shorter and clearer: the negative sign in that equation means that the rate of change of flux in the loop is the *opposite* of boreal to the direction of induced current.

[3] *Boreal* is derived from the rotation of the earth, and signifies a northerly direction compared to the rotation of the earth, or any similar relation between axial direction and rotation. It is from the same root (*boreas*, the north wind) as " aurora borealis." This term is based upon the rotation of the earth as a defining standard, as are Faraday's terms anode and cathode, from west and east. The opposite of *boreal* is *austral*, as in " Australia."

Equations 169 and 170 relate a surface integral to a line integral, the line integral being taken about the boundary of the surface. Here, again, a convention regarding sign is required. If area is to be considered a vector quantity, represented by a vector normal to the surface, it must be known which sense the vector is to have. In previous chap-

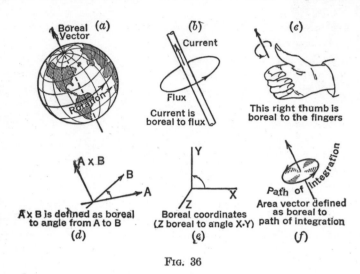

FIG. 36

ters it has been enough to say that the sense of the vector was outward from a closed surface; but in equations 169 and 170 the surface is not a

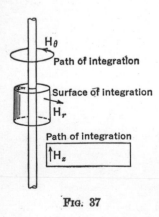

FIG. 37

closed surface, and "outward" has no meaning. When a surface is not closed it has a boundary, and it is sufficient to relate the direction of the area vector to direction around the boundary; the accepted convention is that the boreal direction is positive. Thus in equation 169 the line integral of the left-hand member may be taken in either direction, selected arbitrarily, and this choice of direction around the boundary defines also, by the above convention, the positive sense of area in the right-hand member of the equation. With this convention all ambiguity is removed.

Example. As an example of a solution for a magnetic field, let us compute the field in air about a long straight wire of circular cross section, as in Fig. 35a or 37. The wire is carrying current I (in electrostatic or Gaussian units), and the three components of the magnetic field are to be found.

Equation 167 gives the integral of the magnetic field along any closed path surrounding the wire. First, to apply this equation, let us select a circular path of integration that is concentric with the wire as in Fig. 37. Along this path, **H** is constant; this must be true because of symmetry, for one point on this circle about a circular conductor cannot be distinguished from another.

Call the component of **H** that is tangent to this circular path of integration H_θ. Only this component will contribute to the scalar product of equation 167, so

$$\oint H_\theta \, ds = \frac{4\pi}{c} I \qquad [172]$$

But since, at any constant radius r, H_θ is constant, this becomes

$$H_\theta \oint ds = \frac{4\pi}{c} I \qquad [173]$$

The integral of ds is merely the length of the circular path of integration, and at radius r

$$H_\theta \, 2\pi \, r = \frac{4\pi}{c} I \qquad [174]$$

from which

$$H_\theta = \frac{1}{c} \frac{2I}{r} \qquad [175]$$

Call the component of **H** that is parallel to the axis of the wire H_z. If such a component exists it must, because of symmetry, be equal at all points that are equal radial distances from the wire.

Then call the component of **H** that is in a radial direction H_r. Consider a surface around the conductor and coaxial with it, the general shape of a tin can. That is, the surface is a closed surface, composed of a cylindrical section and two circular plane sections as in Fig. 37. It is desired to obtain $\int \mathbf{B} \cdot d\mathbf{a}$ over this surface for use in equation 163.

Since H_θ does not intersect this surface it contributes nothing to $\int \mathbf{B} \cdot d\mathbf{a}$.

The axial component H_z contributes nothing to $\int \mathbf{B} \cdot d\mathbf{a}$, for, being equal at equal radial distances from the conductor, if it adds to the integral over one plane surface, it subtracts an equal amount over the other, and it does not intersect the cylindrical surface. If the radial component

H_r existed, however, it would give $\int \mathbf{B} \cdot d\mathbf{a}$ over this tin-can-like surface some value different from zero. Since equation 163 says $\int \mathbf{B} \cdot d\mathbf{a}$ is always zero, it follows, when all possible tin-can-like surfaces are considered, that H_r must be zero everywhere.

It remains to evaluate H_z. Consider a line of integration as indicated in Fig. 37. It is rectangular in shape. One of the sides is parallel to the axis of the wire and is fairly close to the wire; the other parallel side is unlimitedly far away. When integrating $\mathbf{H} \cdot d\mathbf{s}$ around this rectangle, nothing is contributed to the integral by H_θ, which is everywhere normal to the path. It has been shown that $H_r = 0$. There remains only H_z, which will (if it exists) contribute to the integral along the short sides of the path.

The total integral around the path is zero, for the path links no current (equation 167). The contribution of H_z to the integral must therefore be zero, and this is possible only if H_z has the same value near the conductor that it has at an unlimited distance, or if $H_z = 0$. Since it is impossible that a conductor carrying finite current should produce a uniform magnetic field through infinite space (for this would require infinite energy) it must be concluded that H_z, as well as H_r, is zero.

Finally, therefore, we determine that only H_θ exists, and its value is given by equation 175. The solution of this simple problem has been carried out in great detail because it illustrates the use of special paths of integration for reaching conclusions regarding magnetic and electric fields.

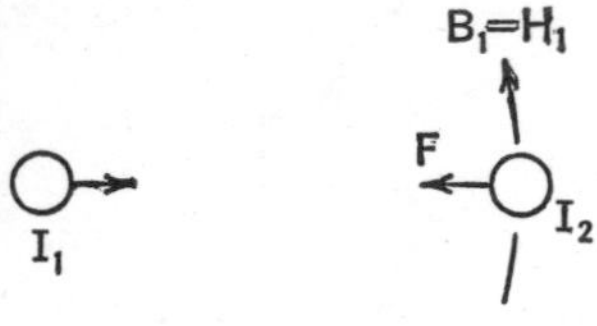

FORCE BETWEEN CURRENTS. In Experiment VI it was found that there is a mechanical force on a conductor that carries current in the neighborhood of another conductor also carrying current. The effect must be mutual, and each current exerts a force on the other. The amount of this force can now be determined.

FIG. 38

The determination of force between parallel wires is simplest, and will be illustrated here. The same method can be applied, if desired, to the general case of any conductors.

Figure 38 shows a cross section of two conductors. Currents I_1 and I_2 are flowing in the conductors, both being directed out of the page. If the distance between the two conductors is d, the magnetic field produced by I_1 at the distance of conductor 2 is (by equation 175)

$$B_1 = H_1 = \frac{1}{c} \frac{2I_1}{d} \qquad [176]$$

The direction of this field is normal to a line connecting the two conductors, as shown in the figure. There is a mechanical force on conductor 2 as given by equation 154, and when equation 176 is substituted into equation 154 it is seen that the magnitude of the force is

$$F = \frac{I_2 L_2}{c} \frac{1}{c} \frac{2I_1}{d} = \frac{1}{c^2} \frac{2I_1 I_2}{d} L_2 \qquad [177]$$

or the force per unit length of conductor 2 is

$$\frac{F}{L_2} = \frac{2I_1 I_2}{c^2 d} \qquad [178]$$

This is a scalar equation. It gives magnitude of force only. The vector product $L{\times}B$ in equation 154 is here equal in magnitude to the product of the scalar magnitudes L and B, because L and B are normal to each other; the direction of force is given by the direction of this vector product, and since, in Fig. 38, L is out of the page (corresponding to the direction of flow of current), and B is up, F, being boreal to the angle from L to B, is directed toward conductor 1.

The force in equation 178 is in dynes if currents are in Gaussian or electrostatic units and distances are in centimeters, with c having the same value as in other equations of this chapter. If currents are expressed in electromagnetic units, however, c is unity. This equation is, indeed, the definition of the electromagnetic system of units: the electromagnetic unit of current is defined as being the amount that will make $c = 1$ in equation 178.

It is evident that equation 178 gives also the magnitude of the force exerted on conductor 1 by the current in conductor 2. The direction of such a force is toward conductor 2. Therefore we have determined that two conductors carrying current in the same direction attract each other, the amount of force being given by equation 178. This is a simple form of **Ampère's law.** As given here it assumes that the spacing between conductors is large compared to the diameter of either conductor and that the conductors are straight and parallel for an unlimited distance.

If either current were reversed in direction, changing the sign of I in equation 154, the direction of the force between conductors would be reversed and would become repulsive. But if both currents were reversed there would again be attraction. From this has arisen the easily remembered but somewhat loose statement that " like currents attract, unlike currents repel."

MAGNETIC FLUX LINKAGES. Current flowing in a coil of wire, as in Fig. 35c, produces a magnetic field. The configuration of the field is such that flux lines extend axially through the coil and return, rather widely dispersed, in outer space.   Each flux line thus passes at least once, and possibly several times, through a surface bounded by the conductor.   Such a surface in Fig. 35c can be visualized as a sheet of rubber with its edge attached to the conductor.   When the wire is bent into a helix the rubber sheet is stretched into a complicated shape that can be imagined more readily than it can be drawn or described.   The closed line shown in Fig. 35c might represent a flux line; such a line passes three times through the surface bounded by the conductor.   It will be recognized that each penetration of this surface by the flux line is equivalent to the ordinary concept of a " flux linkage."

MAGNETIC ENERGY.   Energy is required when the magnetic field is produced.   The energy comes from the electric circuit, as follows. When current starts to flow in a circuit it produces a magnetic field (equation 166).   As the magnetic field grows it induces an electric field in and near the region of the magnetic field; the integral of this electric field along the circuit is electromotive force (equation 159).   An increasing magnetic field induces electromotive force in the circuit in such a direction that it opposes the increase of current.[4]   This induced electromotive force must be overcome by the applied voltage.   It is readily shown that the product of current, voltage, and time is energy.   Thus energy is taken from the circuit as the magnetic field is produced.   An equal amount of energy is returned to the circuit when current ceases to flow, as the magnetic field dies away.

It is assumed that energy taken from the electric circuit during the formation of a magnetic field is stored throughout that field.   If magnetic energy density is taken to be $\mu H^2/8\pi$, total energy existing in a magnetic field is

$$\text{Magnetic energy} = \frac{\mu}{8\pi} \int_{\infty} H^2 \, dv \qquad [179]$$

Since it can be shown that this is equal to the total energy required to establish a magnetic field, the assumed value of energy density is justified.

It will be seen by comparison with equation 122 that the expression for magnetic energy is quite analogous to that for electrostatic energy.

THEORIES.   There are two theories of the magnetic behavior of materials.   These are rather closely analogous to the two theories of dielectric behavior considered in Chapter V.   One theory considers the magnetic intensity **H**, produced by electric current or by a permanent

---

[4] Thus Lenz's law is deduced from equations 159 and 166.

magnet, to be a kind of magnetic driving force, and **B** is considered the resulting magnetic flux density. Permeability, then, is a measure of the ease with which flux can be produced in a given material. Consistent with this concept, the line integral of **H** is called magnetomotive force. Magnetomotive force is considered to be analogous to electromotive force in an electric circuit, in which case **B** is analogous to current density and flux to current. Or, by an entirely different analogy, **H** may be considered analogous to electric field strength **E**, and **B** analogous to electric displacement **D**.

Because of analogies to familiar concepts, this theory of magnetic behavior is very convenient for visualizing magnetic fields and quite useful in computation. But for theoretical purposes and for gaining a true understanding of the physical processes underlying magnetic behavior, an entirely different concept is generally accepted.

In this alternative theory, only **B** exists. This is the magnetic field, and it is everywhere identical with **H** provided *all currents* are taken into account. This includes currents *within* the atomic structure of matter, as well as ordinary currents that are carried by electrons between the atoms of conducting material. Let us consider iron first, because it is an extreme case.

It is believed that material is made of atoms, and that each atom consists of a nucleus with electrons about it. Because of electronic rotations and revolutions, which constitute circulating currents within the atom, some atoms are equivalent to small loops carrying current and will produce magnetic fields. This is true in paramagnetic materials with ferromagnetic substances as extreme examples.

In ordinary iron the many atoms are oriented at random, and although each atom is a small circuit forever carrying current, a piece of iron containing a great number of atoms is on the whole not a magnet. However, if it is placed in an external magnetic field there is a force on each atom that tends to orient all atoms the same way. Then, in an extreme case of polarization, all the many sub-atomic electric currents will cooperate in strengthening the electric field that caused their orientation. This results in a total magnetic field that is tremendously stronger than can be accounted for by electric current in the external circuit alone, which serves mainly to orient the iron atoms.

DIAMAGNETIC MATERIALS. A word must be said about diamagnetic materials, although diamagnetism is an extremely slight effect. It is supposed to result from what may be considered induced currents within the atoms of material.

Figure 39 shows a coil of wire to which a battery may be connected, and a ring of highly conductive material. When the battery is connected to the coil a magnetic field is produced part of which links with the ring. Formation of such a field through the ring induces electromotive force in the ring, and current flows; the result of this induced current in the ring is to weaken the magnetic field produced by the coil. If the material of the ring had perfect conductivity, current induced in the ring would flow as long as there was current in the coil, and the total magnetic field would be always less intense than it would have been in the absence of the ring.

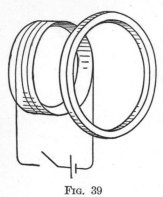

Fig. 39

It is believed that electrons within atoms of material substance act like the ring of Fig. 39. When a magnetic field is produced their motion will be altered, producing the equivalent of a demagnetizing current. Hence the magnetic field in the material is weaker than it would have been in free space, and the material is diamagnetic.

This effect is quite independent of the orientation of polar atoms which constitutes paramagnetism. In fact, it is supposed that all materials are diamagnetic, but that some have also a paramagnetic tendency, and that the latter effect is in many cases more marked than the former with the result that the material is on the whole paramagnetic or even ferromagnetic.

The demagnetizing circulating current of diamagnetism is always extremely small, as it affects the magnetic field by only a few parts in a million.

PROBLEMS

1. Would it be possible to *define* magnetic field strength as a vector *parallel* to the magnetic force on the exploring wire of Fig. 32?

2. What is the direction of the magnetic field in Fig. 32 if current is flowing downward in the exploring wire? Check with equation 154.

3. If magnetic flux links a coil of wire of several turns, the voltage induced in the coil by a change of flux is proportional to the number of turns. How is this expressed by equation 159? What is the surface of integration for that equation in such a case?

4. There are ten turns of wire wound in a layer on a wooden spool, and a current of 5 amperes flows in the wire. Ten more turns are then wound close upon the first layer, and current is passed through all turns in the same direction around the spool. With the added turns, current is reduced to 4 amperes. Using equation 169 with a path of integration passing axially through the spool, find how much the magnetic field near the center of the spool is changed. Draw a sketch showing the direction of current, the direction of flux, and the path of integration of equation 169.

5. Show that the magnetic field at a radius r within a copper conductor carrying current I is $\dfrac{2Ir}{cr_0^2}$. The radius of the cylindrical conductor is r_0, which is of course greater than r. Current is uniformly distributed across the conductor cross section: Discuss units.

6. Find the curl of the magnetic field of Problem 5. Does it agree with equation 171?

7. Find and plot the variation of magnetic vector potential along a radial line passing through the center of the conductor of Problem 5. Show, in a single curve, the intensity of the vector potential both within and outside the conductor.

8. How is the magnetizing current of a transformer related to the number of turns of the primary winding, if there is no change of the general dimensions of the transformer or of the applied alternating voltage? From which equations do you reach this result?

Chapter VIII

EXAMPLES AND INTERPRETATION

Most of the physical relations that have been discussed in the previous chapters are familiar. They are simple laws of electrostatics, magnetic flux, the steady flow of current, and induced voltage. If they have appeared strange it is because they have been generalized to apply to the broadest possible range of conditions. These generalized relationships have something in common with disembodied spirits, and seem unsubstantial to most of us until they are attached to concrete situations. The unaccustomed notation of vector analysis has done nothing to relieve this situation, although it has done a great deal to save us from wandering in a maze of differential equations.

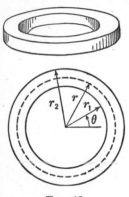

FIG. 40

The purpose of this chapter is to supply a few concrete illustrations. There will be no new experimental evidence.

Example 1. A solenoidal coil of many turns of fine wire is wound on a wooden core, the shape of which is shown in Fig. 40. The core is a ring of rectangular cross section. There are N turns of wire wound upon it, each carrying current I. It is desired to find the magnetic field produced by the current, and the inductance of the coil.

Cylindrical coordinates may best be used for reference, with the Z axis coinciding with the axis of the ring. The radius of the inner surface of the ring is r_1 and of the outer surface r_2.

From the symmetrical arrangement of the current and from the known nature of the magnetic field it is apparent that the magnetic field in this case will be circular. That is, H_θ will exist, but H_r and H_z will be zero.[1] This could be proved, of course, but time will be saved if it is accepted without proof.

---

[1] If there is a single layer of turns of wire wound on the core, so that the current follows once around the core while spiraling through the winding, there will be a small component of field (H_z) passing vertically through the space within the core. If a double-layer winding is used this may be completely eliminated, and in any coil it may usually be neglected.

To find the strength of the field, consider a circle of radius r (shown by the dash circle in Fig. 40), to be the path of integration for equation 169:

$$\oint \mathbf{H} \cdot d\mathbf{s} = \frac{4\pi}{c} \int \iota \cdot d\mathbf{a} \qquad [169]$$

With the line integral on the left-hand side of this equation taken around the circle of radius r, the right-hand member gives the total current passing through the space within the circle. If r is less than r_1 and lies within the ring, or if r is greater than r_2, or if the circular path of integration lies above the ring or below it, no current passes within the circle. In such a case $\mathbf{H}$ is zero, and there is no magnetic field in these regions.

But if the circle lies within the coil, as shown in the figure, the current I passes N times through any surface bounded by the circle, and

$$\oint \mathbf{H} \cdot d\mathbf{s} = \frac{4\pi}{c} NI \qquad [180]$$

By symmetry, the value of $\mathbf{H}$ is constant along a circular path that is, like the one under consideration, concentric with the ring, and since only H_θ exists it follows that

$$H_\theta \oint ds = 2\pi r H_\theta = \frac{4\pi NI}{c} \qquad [181]$$

from which

$$H_\theta = \frac{2NI}{cr} \qquad [182]$$

According to this equation the magnetic field is not uniform within the coil, but is stronger nearer the inner surface, the field strength being inversely proportional to the radius.

It may be recognized that $\int \mathbf{H} \cdot d\mathbf{s}$ is **magnetic potential difference** (magnetic scalar potential), analogous to electric potential difference or voltage. The magnetic potential difference around a closed path, as in equation 180, is commonly given the name **magnetomotive force** (see page 81).

Let us compute the amount of flux within the solenoidal coil. To find the total flux we integrate $\mathbf{B}$ over the cross section of the core. Since the coil is wound on a wooden core, $\mathbf{B} = \mathbf{H}$, and the desired value is

$$\Phi = \int \mathbf{B} \cdot d\mathbf{a} = \int H_\theta \, da \qquad [183]$$

If the thickness of the core parallel to the Z axis is z_1,

$$\Phi = \int_{r_1}^{r_2} \frac{2NI}{cr} z_1 \, dr = \frac{2z_1 NI}{c} \ln \frac{r_2}{r_1} \qquad [184]$$

Now the inductance of the coil can be determined. The **inductance** is, by definition,

$$L = \frac{cN\Phi}{I} \qquad [185]$$

The factor c appears when the definition is written, as here, in Gaussian units. Φ is the flux that passes through a single turn of the conductor and is therefore the flux in the core. Substituting equation 184 into 185, the inductance of the toroidal coil is

$$L = \frac{cN\Phi}{I} = 2N^2 z_1 \ln \frac{r_2}{r_1} \qquad [186]$$

This inductance is in Gaussian units, abhenrys, or millimicrohenrys. The symbol ln indicates the natural logarithm.

BOUNDARY SURFACES. When either an electric or a magnetic field passes from one substance into another, as does the magnetic field when entering a piece of iron or the electric field when passing from air to oil, there is a peculiar set of conditions at the surface that separates one material from the other.

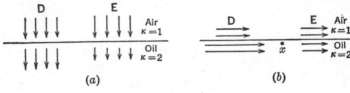

FIG. 41

As an example, consider an electric field partly in air and partly in oil, shown in Fig. 41. (In this diagram the field intensity is shown by the lengths of the vectors of E and D, rather than by their spacing as in the usual convention.) In Fig. 41a an electric field is normal to the surface between air ($\kappa = 1$) and oil ($\kappa = 2$).

Vectors of D are on the left. Since Experiment IV has shown that the divergence of D is everywhere zero, the magnitude of D must be the same just within the oil as it is just above the surface. On the right, E is shown. It is half as great in the oil as in the air, being equal to D/κ.

Figure 41b shows the same boundary surface with an electric field parallel to the surface. In this case **E**, as shown on the right, must be the same within the oil as in the air. This is necessary in order to have zero curl of **E** at the surface. **D**, therefore, is twice as great in the oil as in the air.

The necessity for zero curl of **E** at the surface follows from Experiment II, but it may be shown specifically for this particular case. Consider a small charged particle just below the surface of the oil, at the point marked x in Fig. 41b. This particle is to be moved to the right a distance of 1 inch, always just below the surface. It is then raised into the air and moved just above the surface until it is directly over the point x. It is then lowered to its original position. Work is done on the particle by the electric field while it is being moved toward the right in the oil. External work must be exerted on the particle to move it back, toward the left, in air. No work is done either with or against electrostatic forces in lifting the particle out of oil or in lowering it in again, both because such motion is normal to the electrostatic force and because the distance of such motion may be as little as desired. To maintain conservation of energy the energy received moving from left to right must equal the energy delivered moving from right to left, and therefore the force on the particle in oil must be equal to the force in air. If this were not so, a perpetual-motion machine could easily be devised. But if the forces are equal the electric field strengths **E** must be equal above the surface and below, by equation 2.

It may be noted that the curl of **D** is not zero at such a boundary. It is, indeed, infinite.

In the above paragraphs electric fields normal and tangential to the boundary surface have been considered. Since any field may be resolved into normal and tangential components at a boundary, the behavior of any field is deduced from the general relations that have been proved: *At a boundary between materials of different dielectric constant* (1) the *normal* component of **D** is continuous; (2) the *tangential* component of **E** is continuous.

This may readily be explained in terms of the theory of polarization of dielectric materials, for part of the normal component of **E** terminates on charge of polarization at the surface of the oil, even though there is no *free* charge present. (**D**, according to this theory, is a mathematical fiction that is defined as $\mathbf{D} = \kappa\mathbf{E}$ in order to establish a field that is *by definition* continuous at a boundary between dielectric materials.) Surface charge of polarization cannot affect the tangential component of electric field, and consequently the tangential component is continuous at a boundary.

Similarly it is seen that the normal component of magnetic flux density **B** is continuous at a boundary between materials of different permeability, for it must have no divergence at any point. The tangential component of **H** is continuous at such a boundary if there is no current flowing at the boundary surface, for in the absence of current the curl of **H** must be zero.

When current flows in a conductor there is no curl in the magnetic field surrounding the conductor, but within the conducting material the magnetic field has curl for, as was considered in the previous chapter, curl is proportional to current density. There can never at any place be a *discontinuity* of the magnetic field strength **H** — no sudden change, for instance, from a finite value to zero — for a discontinuity results in infinite curl, and can appear only at a surface with *infinite* current density. In a later chapter infinite current density is assumed in a perfectly conducting material; this represents an idealized condition that can be approached but never attained, for no physical material is perfectly conducting.

Another important surface condition is at a boundary between a non-conducting medium, such as air, and a conductor, such as copper. Within the conductor the electric field must be proportional to current density, and in the direction of current flow. A component of **E** tangential to the surface will exist within the conductor if there is current flowing. An equal tangential component of **E** must also exist in space just beyond the surface of the conductor; if it did not, the electric field would have a discontinuity at the surface, with infinite curl, and this is impossible.

Therefore the conclusion is: *At a surface between materials of different conductivity the tangential component of* **E** *is continuous.*

Example 2. Figure 42 shows an old-fashioned carbon filament for an electric light. The thickness of the filament is exaggerated so that arrows may be drawn to show the electric field within the filament. A steady current is flowing through the filament, and it is desired to find the electric field that exists.

Within the filament there is uniform current density, flowing everywhere parallel to the surface of the conducting filament, and since electric field strength is proportional to current density (equation 133) the electric field is also directed along the filament and is uniform in magnitude. If the filament is 10 inches long and the applied voltage is 110 volts, the electric field strength within the filament is everywhere 11 volts per inch. This field is in no way affected by turns and twists of the filament, and the same situation exists in any wire of uniform cross section that is carrying steady current. In a conductor that is not carrying current there is no electric field.

This last statement might seem contradictory to the fact that an electric field may be induced in a conducting rod that is not part of a circuit and hence cannot carry a steady flow of current. But let us suppose a copper rod, as shown in Fig. 43, is in a changing magnetic field that induces an electromotive force upward in the rod. At the instant

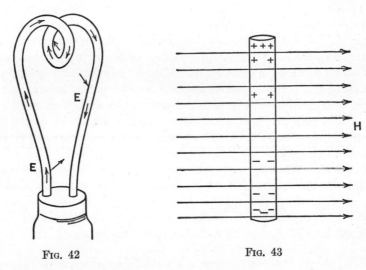

FIG. 42   FIG. 43

the magnetic field begins to induce electromotive force there will be an electric field in the copper, and for an instant current will flow. Almost at once, however, enough positive charge will accumulate at the top of the rod, and enough negative charge at the bottom, to produce a field equal and opposite to the induced field, and the charge will distribute itself in exactly the right manner to give zero resultant electric field within the copper and there will then be zero current. Although there is no field within the rod in such a case, it does not follow that there is zero electric field elsewhere. There will, indeed, be electric flux emanating from the top of the rod and returning at the bottom, and a voltmeter (if its leads were not in the changing magnetic field) would indicate the value of the induced electromotive force.

Returning to consideration of the electric-light filament, there will be electric field also in the space about the filament. There is a potential difference of 110 volts between the two ends of the filament, so there must be electric field in the intervening space. This emanates from charge located on the surface of the filament; charge that was driven at the instant voltage was applied to the filament by a component of field within the filament normal to the filament surface. When this charge reached its final position in proper amount the normal component of field *within* the filament was reduced to zero, and thereafter the surface charge remained constant.

The electric field in space around the filament is quite complicated. There is a component normal to the surface, due to the surface charge. There is a component tangential to the surface, equal to the field within the filament, for it was seen that the tangential component of electric field is continuous at a surface. The geometry of the filament is not simple, and we will not attempt any quantitative solution of this problem, but merely note that the line integral of $\mathbf{E} \cdot d\mathbf{s}$ from any point on the filament to another point on the filament, following any path, must be equal to the potential difference between those two points, and the electric field strength will be distributed so as to make this true. The electric field in space near the surface of the filament, particularly at the ends of the filament, may have an intensity of thousands of volts per inch.

Example 3.   When current is changed in the toroidal coil of Example 1 (Fig. 40) the magnetic field is changed proportionately, and the changing magnetic field induces an electric field in and around the toroid.   Equation 161 tells us that the induced electric field has curl within the core of the toroid, the amount of curl being

$$\nabla \times \mathbf{E} = -\frac{1}{c}\frac{\partial \mathbf{B}}{\partial t} \tag{187}$$

Integrating each side of this equation over the cross section area of the coil, and applying Stokes' theorem to the left-hand member, gives

$$\int \nabla \times \mathbf{E} \cdot d\mathbf{a} = \oint \mathbf{E} \cdot d\mathbf{s} = -\frac{1}{c}\frac{\partial}{\partial t}\int \mathbf{B} \cdot d\mathbf{a} \tag{188}$$

The second member of this equation is a line integral of electric field. For our purposes we select a path of integration that surrounds the core of the solenoid; it may be practically identical with one turn of the winding that is wrapped upon the core. The integral of induced electric field along such a path is the electromotive force induced in one turn of the coil (as in equation 159); and there are N turns. The surface integral in the right-hand member of equation 188 is, from equation 155, the magnetic flux through the core. So the total electromotive force induced in all N turns is

$$\text{Electromotive force} = -\frac{N}{c}\frac{\partial \Phi}{\partial t} \tag{189}$$

This is a familiar equation. Another familiar form results when the definition of inductance given in equation 185 is substituted into equation 189, giving

$$\text{Electromotive force} = -\frac{L}{c^2}\frac{\partial I}{\partial t} \qquad [190]$$

The factor c^2 appears in this equation because, in the Gaussian system, the electromotive force is in statvolts and I is in statamperes, although L is in abhenrys. The negative sign indicates that if the current is increasing, so that the rate of change of current is positive, the induced electromotive force is negative and opposes the flow of current.

Example 4. When a magnetic field is changing it induces an electric field even in empty space, as discussed in Chapter VII. The electric field so induced is capable of exerting force on any charged particles that exist in the region of changing magnetic field, and this principle is used[2] in the "induction accelerator" to drive electrons for "atom-smashing" purposes.

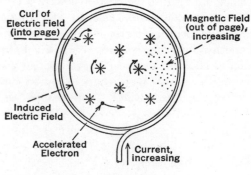

FIG. 44

Consider a narrow evacuated space between the large, round, flat faces of iron magnetic poles. The evacuated space is rather disk-like, thin from top to bottom, but large in diameter, and a strong magnetic field passes through the thickness of it from the magnetic pole face above to the magnetic pole face below. The magnetic field is produced by current flowing in many turns of wire about the iron field structure (see Fig. 44).

Now consider that current through the winding can be increased from zero to some given value in a very small fraction of a second (1/600 second); the magnetic field in the evacuated space will in-

[2] "Acceleration of Electrons by Magnetic Induction," D. W. Kerst, *Physical Review*, volume 60, July 1, 1941, pages 47–53.

crease at a correspondingly rapid rate. This will induce an electric field in the space, and electrons or other charged particles released into the evacuated space will have force exerted on them and will be accelerated in a more or less spiral path, gaining velocity.

As a first approximation we may consider that the magnetic field is uniform in the region directly between pole faces, falling suddenly to zero as one passes out from between the iron plates. This is not truly correct, for it is impossible to have an abrupt change from a region of magnetic field to a region of no magnetic field; an abrupt change of magnetic field strength implies infinite curl in the magnetic field (consider the " curl-meter " of Chapter II). In the actual case of magnetic field between pole faces there will be, as is well known, " fringing " of the lines of force, allowing the field strength to decrease gradually to zero without curl.

Where the magnetic field is changing with time there will be curl of the electric field (equation 161) and the next step of the problem is to find the electric field. When current in the winding is changed there is a change of magnetic field in the space between pole faces, and since the field is increasing in intensity without changing in direction it follows that the rate of change is in the same direction as the field itself. The curl of **E** is, therefore, by equation 161, also uniform and in the opposite direction. The problem is to find an electric field that has such a curl in the circular region between magnets and no curl elsewhere.

Visualize a battery of paddle-wheel " curl-meters " as in Fig. 44, all turning at the same speed and in the same direction. It is apparent that their rotation may be caused by an electric field revolving as a whirlpool with the greatest intensity at the circumference. It will be well to be definite regarding direction.

If an increasing magnetic field is produced by a counterclockwise current in the field winding, as indicated, the magnetic field, being boreal to the current, will be out of the page. Because of the negative sign in equation 161, the curl of the electric field will be into the page, and the circulation of the electric field, being boreal to its curl, will be clockwise. Note that it is this same clockwise field that, induced in the conductor of the field winding, opposes the increase of current according to Lenz's law.

Assuming cylindrical coordinates with the Z axis coinciding with the axis of the magnetic poles, the electric field is in the negative θ direction. Let us assume it to be proportional to r:

$$E_\theta = -Ar \qquad [191]$$

The value of A is to be determined; but it is not a function of r, θ, or z.

From Table II the curl of the electric field is

$$\nabla \times \mathbf{E} = -\mathbf{k}\left(A + \frac{Ar}{r}\right) = -\mathbf{k}\,2A \qquad [192]$$

and from equation 161

$$\frac{1}{c}\frac{\partial \mathbf{B}}{\partial t} = \mathbf{k}\,2A \quad \text{or} \quad \frac{1}{c}\frac{\partial B}{\partial t} = 2A \qquad [193]$$

This evaluates A for use in equation 191, and it follows that between the magnetic pole pieces

$$E_\theta = -\frac{r}{2c}\frac{\partial B}{\partial t} \qquad [194]$$

Although proportionality between field strength and radius was merely assumed in equation 191, the correctness of the assumption is proved by showing that equation 161 is satisfied by the electric field of equation 194 and the given magnetic field of uniform distribution.

The induced electric field has its maximum value at a radius r_0 equal to the outer radius of the magnetic field. The electric field does not then cease abruptly, but dies away at radii greater than r_0 in such a manner that the electric field has no curl. (This would be but slightly modified if fringing of the magnetic field were considered.) To determine the electric field that lies in outer space beyond the magnetic field, it is necessary to find a field that (1) has no curl, (2) is continuous with the field of equation 194 at radius r_0, and (3) vanishes at infinite radius. Conditions (1) and (3) are satisfied by

$$E_\theta = -\frac{A'}{r} \qquad [195]$$

At radius r_0 this must be equal to equation 194, so

$$\frac{A'}{r_0} = \frac{r_0}{2c}\frac{\partial B}{\partial t}$$

From this the value of A' can be determined, and, in the outer region

$$E_\theta = -\frac{r_0{}^2}{2cr}\frac{\partial B}{\partial t} \qquad [196]$$

Equation 196 follows from an assumption of unlimited empty space. In fact, of course, the magnetic field structure and other apparatus must interfere with this ideal condition, and equation 196 is a more or less accurate approximation of the electric field at radii that are not too much greater than r_0.

It is very interesting to compare the electric fields that, in this example, result from a changing magnetic field with the magnetic fields that were shown in Chapter VII to result from current in a long straight wire. The field distributions in and around a long conductor are strictly analogous to those of equations 194 and 196 respectively.[3]

Equations 194 and 196 are not the only possible solutions of equation 161 within the regions under consideration. In fact any electric field without curl could be added to these solutions, and the sum would also be a solution of the equation. (A field without curl is, in this case, analogous to a constant of integration.) But there simply *is* no field that is without curl and without divergence and that becomes zero at an infinite distance and is nowhere of infinite strength. Within these obvious physical limitations our solutions are the only ones that satisfy both the electromagnetic equations and the boundary conditions.

One factor, however, has been neglected. It is safe to do so in this case, for its quantitative importance is insignificant. But in other examples it will be found to be the only important part of the solution. It is **radiation.** When the changing magnetic field produces an electric field about the magnet a wave of electromagnetic energy travels outward from the apparatus. It carries away from the " induction accelerator " of the present example so small a fraction of the total energy that it is entirely negligible.

But radiation is not always negligible; in radio communication it is the *sine qua non* of practical value. The electromagnetic theory that has been developed in the preceding chapters fails to account for radiation. It deals with electric fields that are **quasi-stationary** — fields, that is, that change so slowly that at any instant they may be regarded as electrostatic.

We have gone farther in magnetics, for we have discovered that the rate of change of a magnetic field is important. A changing magnetic field is capable of producing an electric field. We owe to James Clerk Maxwell the idea that a changing electric field is likewise capable of producing a magnetic field. With the consideration of this additional hypothesis we advance from the quasi-stationary state to the **electrodynamic** state.

PROBLEMS

1. A coil of many turns of fine wire is wound on a long wooden cylinder. There are n turns on each centimeter of length, and each turn of the coil carries current I. The radius of the coil is r. Show that the inductance per unit length of the coil is $39.5 \, r^2 n^2$ abhenrys per centimeter. (Note: This is for an infinitely long coil, but is

---

[3] The reason for the analogy is simply that the two field distributions are parallel solutions of the two Maxwellian equations.

in error by less than 10 per cent if the length of the coil is more than four times its diameter.)

2. A coil is wound on a core as in Example 1, page 92, except that the core is a square frame instead of a ring. Also, the core is iron, not wood. Prove definitely whether or not the magnetic flux can be entirely confined to the iron or will " cut corners " in air.

3. Repeat Example 1, page 92, for a coil wound on a toroidal core of circular cross section. Find the magnetic flux in the core, and the inductance. Check the computed inductance with a value that may be obtained from a handbook.

4. An electric field passes from air into oil ($\kappa = 2$). The field in air is at an angle of 45 degrees to the surface of the oil. What is the angle between the surface and the field in the oil? Find this angle for both D and E.

5. Prove that the field of equation 195 has no curl (as is stated on page 101).

6. There is a potential difference of 100 volts between two large parallel sheets of copper that are 10 centimeters apart in air. Also, current is flowing in each sheet; it flows toward the right in the lower sheet and toward the left in the upper. The IR drop (more explicitly the ratio of current density to conductivity) is uniformly 3 volts per centimeter. Find the electric field in the three regions: (1) above both sheets, (2) below both sheets, and (3) between the sheets.

7. Each sheet of Problem 6 is 0.01 millimeter thick. Find the magnetic field in the same three regions.

Chapter IX

MAXWELL'S HYPOTHESIS

The experimental evidence is now before us. From nine experiments described in the preceding chapters we are fully informed regarding electric and magnetic fields. The results of the experiments are summarized below, and included with them are two assumptions that are, essentially, definitions:

From Experiment I, an electric field is found to exist and is defined.

From Experiment II, the electrostatic field is lamellar (without curl).

From Experiment III, divergence of the electrostatic field is proportional to charge density.

From Experiment IV, the behavior of dielectric substances is known.

From Experiment V, Ohm's law is established.

From Experiment VI, a magnetic field is found to exist, and is defined.

From Experiment VII, a changing magnetic field is found to induce an electric field.

From Experiment VIII, the magnetostatic field is solenoidal (without divergence).

From Experiment IX, the curl of the magnetostatic field is proportional to current density.

It is assumed that the dynamic electric field has divergence proportional to charge density. (This is proved in Experiment III for the *static* electric field only.)

It is assumed that the dynamic magnetic field has no divergence. (This is proved in Experiment VIII for the *static* magnetic field only.

The information obtained from these experiments is the basis of the following discussion of electromagnetism. Either these experiments, or others that yield equivalent data, must be the foundation of any development of electromagnetic theory.

Information regarding electric and magnetic fields was available to scientists about the middle of the nineteenth century. It was not in the mathematical form in which it is given here; indeed the very concept of an electric or magnetic field was at that time a new idea of Faraday's, considered with doubt by most scientists. The important controversy between believers in " action at a distance " and converts to the newly proposed " field theory " was at its height. Of course, electrostatic and magnetostatic fields had been computed and graphically indicated for the better part of a century, but Faraday was the first (according to James Clerk Maxwell) actually to believe in the existence of the electromagnetic field. Previously, fields had been looked upon as convenient means of visualizing the arrangement of forces that resulted from electric and magnetic action, but to Faraday (as to us) the magnetic field was the actual means by which magnetic force was exerted.

From the time of Ampère's work (1820 to 1825) it had been considered that one wire carrying current exerted a force on another wire carrying current, and no intermediate agency for exerting that force was taken into account. This was the action-at-a-distance theory, and it followed logically Newton's famous law of gravitation, then a century old and universally accepted. Newton's law assumed action at a distance, for it did not consider any medium necessary for the transmission of gravitational force. It was only natural that electrical scientists of the early nineteenth century would follow this illustrious precedent.

Faraday, however, conceived the physical reality of electric and magnetic fields, and Maxwell undertook to express the mathematical relationships involved. It was Maxwell who pointed out that a " displacement current " (as in our equation 145) would simplify and improve the mathematical system. Then Maxwell made a most remarkable proposal as follows: It is known by experiment that *conduction* current produces a magnetic field; *total* current is for mathematical purposes best expressed as the sum of conduction current and displacement current; is it not, then, likely that *displacement* current also produces a magnetic field? Experimental technique did not permit this to be either proved or disproved by direct investigation in Maxwell's time, for the quantities involved were too small. But this hypothesis led to a conclusion of fundamental importance, for Maxwell showed that, if it were true, energy would be transmitted as electromagnetic waves.

The action-at-a-distance theory assumed that electrical action appeared instantaneously at all points, however remote. Maxwell's theory, on the other hand, required that energy be transmitted by waves traveling at a finite speed. This speed of wave propagation could be computed. Perhaps some experimental verification of the theory would be obtained by studying the velocity of electromagnetic disturbances.   Before considering experimental evidence we will follow Maxwell's reasoning that leads to electromagnetic waves.

Maxwell's hypothesis was that, in general, when there are varying electric fields, a magnetic field is produced by the sum of the conduction current and the displacement current.   In equation 171, which is

$$\nabla \times \mathbf{H} = \frac{4\pi}{c} \, \iota \qquad [171]$$

the current density, according to Maxwell, is the total current density, and when equation 145 is substituted into 171 it follows that

$$\nabla \times \mathbf{H} = \frac{4\pi}{c} \left(\gamma \mathbf{E} + \frac{\kappa}{4\pi} \frac{\partial \mathbf{E}}{\partial t} \right)$$

$$= \frac{1}{c} \left(4\pi \, \gamma \mathbf{E} + \frac{\partial \mathbf{D}}{\partial t} \right) \qquad [197]$$

This is one of the equations known as **Maxwell's equations.**   The other is equation 161 of Chapter VII:

$$\nabla \times \mathbf{E} = - \frac{1}{c} \frac{\partial \mathbf{B}}{\partial t} \qquad [161]$$

The other two fundamental field equations are

$$\nabla \cdot \mathbf{B} = 0 \qquad [164]$$

$$\nabla \cdot \mathbf{D} = 4\pi \, \rho \qquad [93]$$

These are the basic equations of electromagnetic theory.   They are repeated for ready reference in Table III (inside back cover).

It will be noted that Maxwell's equations become beautifully simple and symmetrical when applied in free space, in which there is no charge, no conductivity, and neither dielectric nor magnetic material.   In free space:

$$\nabla \times \mathbf{H} = \frac{1}{c} \frac{\partial \mathbf{E}}{\partial t} \qquad [198]$$

$$\nabla \times \mathbf{E} = - \frac{1}{c} \frac{\partial \mathbf{H}}{\partial t} \qquad [199]$$

$$\nabla \cdot \mathbf{H} = 0 \qquad [200]$$

$$\nabla \cdot \mathbf{E} = 0 \qquad [201]$$

It will be well to consider once more the physical meaning of these equations.   Equation 198 says that a changing electric field will produce a magnetic field, and equation 199 says that a changing magnetic field will produce an electric field. The latter relation is the familiar principle on which transformers work; the former is Maxwell's hypothesis which says that displacement current as well as conduction current is able to produce a magnetic field. Equation 198 does not contain a term to account for magnetic field produced by actual conduction current because the equation is a simplified one applying to free space only, where there can be no conduction current; equation 197 is the complete equation, and does contain such a term.

But equations 198 and 199 are particularly interesting to consider relative to the propagation of electric waves. It will be seen at once that if a changing electric field produces a changing magnetic field, and that in turn produces an electric field which produces a magnetic field, and so on, some kind of a series of energy transfers is started whenever any electric or magnetic disturbance takes place. Energy will be transferred from the electric field to the magnetic, and back to the electric, and so on indefinitely. If (as is actually true) the magnetic energy does not appear at precisely the same location in space as the electric energy from which it is derived, but a little beyond, and if the electric energy derived from that magnetic energy is again a little farther advanced in space, and so on, so that as the energy is changing from form to form it is also being propagated through space, the result may quite reasonably be expected to be a traveling wave of electromagnetic energy.

Consider a somewhat analogous situation. By some means a small volume of water in the middle of a lake is artificially set into vertical oscillatory motion. Perhaps a bucketful of water is suddenly dumped into the lake. Whatever the character of the disturbance, the surface of the water at that point rises and falls in an oscillatory manner. But it is not possible for the bucketful of water to oscillate independently of the water surrounding it. Its periodic excesses and deficiencies of pressure are transmitted to the surrounding water, which thereby receives energy and is, in turn, put into motion. In its resulting undulation it also transfers energy to the next outer region. By this process a wave is propagated across the surface of the lake.

The fundamental reason for the existence of a water wave is this: the motion and pressure of a given volume of water are not independent of the motion and pressure of the water surrounding that volume, and as the given volume of water is disturbed it transmits energy to the water next to it.

The fundamental reason for the existence of an electric wave is very similar. A changing magnetic field induces an electric field, both in the region in which the magnetic field is changing and also in the surrounding region; likewise a changing electric field produces a magnetic field in the region in which the change takes place and also in the surrounding region.[1] Consequently when there is a disturbance of either the electric or magnetic conditions in a given region of space the disturbance cannot be confined to that space. The changing fields within that region will induce fields in the surrounding region also, and those, in turn, in the next surrounding space, and energy is propagated outward. As this action continues a wave of electromagnetic energy is transmitted.

When there is an excess of electromagnetic energy in unbounded space it cannot stand still, any more than a mound of water can be stationary on the surface of a lake. It cannot merely subside. It can only travel as a wave until the energy is dissipated.

To show that this is indeed the action prescribed by Maxwell's equations, we will develop from them the so-called **wave equations.** We have two equations to begin with, each of which contains both **E** and **H**, and the first step is to solve the equations simultaneously in order to eliminate one of the variables and retain the other. Let us eliminate **H** and thereby obtain an equation in which the only variables are **E** and time. Such an equation will be more easily interpreted.

Before going farther it is well to remark that Maxwell's equations are partial differential equations. Equation 199, for example, equates the rate of change of electric field through space (the curl) to the rate of change of magnetic field with time. It is too much, therefore, to hope for any single simple solution, for that is not commonly to be obtained from simultaneous partial differential equations. As in all problems involving such equations, boundary conditions are all important.

It was stated above that, according to equation 198, a changing electric field will produce a magnetic field. Strictly, the equation says that a changing electric field will produce a space derivative (curl) of a magnetic field. But it is obvious that if a magnetic field has some value of curl, and therefore varies from point to point in space, it cannot everywhere be zero. Since curl of **H** cannot exist without **H** also existing, we may safely say that a changing electric field produces a magnetic field.

---

[1] Perhaps it is helpful to think of it this way: current flowing in a wire produces magnetic field in the wire, but it also produces magnetic field in space around the wire — space in which no current is flowing. Similarly, displacement current (which results from a changing electric field) produces magnetic field in the region in which displacement current exists (where the electric field is changing) and also in the surrounding region.

Now we are ready to proceed with the simultaneous solution of equations 198 and 199. First take the curl of each side of equation 199, giving

$$\nabla\times(\nabla\times E) = -\frac{1}{c}\,\nabla\times\frac{\partial H}{\partial t} \qquad [202]$$

On the right-hand side of this equation it may be noted that the curl, which is a partial derivative with respect to distance, operates on a partial derivative with respect to time. It is a well-known mathematical principle that the order of partial differentiation makes no difference, and therefore

$$\nabla\times(\nabla\times E) = -\frac{1}{c}\,\frac{\partial}{\partial t}\,(\nabla\times H) \qquad [203]$$

(If this is not clear, expand the curl in rectangular coordinates.)

But the curl of H is known from equation 198 and may be substituted into equation 203, giving

$$\nabla\times(\nabla\times E) = -\frac{1}{c}\,\frac{\partial}{\partial t}\left(\frac{1}{c}\,\frac{\partial E}{\partial t}\right) = -\frac{1}{c^2}\,\frac{\partial^2 E}{\partial t^2} \qquad [204]$$

This equation is entirely in E, as desired, but it may be simplified.

The left-hand member of equation 204 is the curl of the curl of a vector. It may be shown as a general mathematical relation that the curl of the curl of any vector is equal to the gradient of the divergence of that vector minus the Laplacian. This is, indeed, analogous to equation 28, page 18. Symbolically,

$$\nabla\times(\nabla\times A) = \nabla(\nabla\cdot A) - \nabla^2 A \qquad [205]$$

If this theorem is applied to the magnetic field, as in equation 204, it is simplified by the fact that the divergence of the electric field in free space is everywhere zero, and the first term of the expansion drops out. This leaves simply

$$\nabla^2 E = \frac{1}{c^2}\,\frac{\partial^2 E}{\partial t^2} \qquad [206]$$

To some readers equation 206 will be a familiar form, recognizable as a wave equation. To others its nature will be clearer if the vector quantities are expanded in Cartesian form:

$$\frac{\partial^2 E_x}{\partial x^2} + \frac{\partial^2 E_x}{\partial y^2} + \frac{\partial^2 E_x}{\partial z^2} = \frac{1}{c^2}\,\frac{\partial^2 E_x}{\partial t^2}$$

$$\frac{\partial^2 E_y}{\partial x^2} + \frac{\partial^2 E_y}{\partial y^2} + \frac{\partial^2 E_y}{\partial z^2} = \frac{1}{c^2}\,\frac{\partial^2 E_y}{\partial t^2} \qquad [207]$$

$$\frac{\partial^2 E_z}{\partial x^2} + \frac{\partial^2 E_z}{\partial y^2} + \frac{\partial^2 E_z}{\partial z^2} = \frac{1}{c^2}\,\frac{\partial^2 E_z}{\partial t^2}$$

If a simple special case is now considered in which E_x and E_z do not exist and with E_y a function of x but not of y or z, the equations 207 reduce to

$$E_x = 0 \quad E_z = 0$$

$$\frac{\partial^2 E_y}{\partial x^2} = \frac{1}{c^2} \frac{\partial^2 E_y}{\partial t^2} \qquad [208]$$

Each of the restrictions leading to equation 208 has a physical meaning that will be discussed in a later chapter.

Equation 208 is the simplest form of the traveling-wave differential equation. Its solution is

$$E_y = f(x - ct) \qquad [209]$$

wherein $f(x - ct)$ represents any function of the quantity $(x - ct)$. (Equation 208 has other solutions also, one of which is $f_2(x + ct)$. We are not at present interested in these other solutions.) To prove that equation 209 is a solution of equation 208, it may be substituted into that equation and the indicated differentiations performed, as in Problem 5.

It is now necessary to recognize that equation 209 describes a transverse wave of constant size and shape that is traveling in the positive direction along the X axis with velocity c. Readers to whom this is unfamiliar will find it helpful to consider specific functions of $(x - ct)$ and to plot $f(x)$ for a number of successive values of time.

For instance, consider the following special case of equation 209 in which the function is taken to be sinusoidal:

$$E_y = \sin(x - ct)$$

Figure 45 shows one cycle of this wave, plotted as a function of x for several different values of time. In other words, if the wave as it traveled through space were visible, Fig. 45 would be a succession of snapshots of it, taken at the instants at which ct equals 0, $\pi/6$, $\pi/3$, and $\pi/2$. It is apparent from the equation that all these will be sine curves of the same shape and amplitude. But the curve for which $ct = \pi/6$ will be displaced with reference to the one for which $ct = 0$, and each of its corresponding values will occur at a value of x greater by $\pi/6$. That is, to keep the quantity in parentheses unchanged, and therefore to have the same value of E_y, x will have to increase as time increases. The result will be a wave moving from left to right as time passes. Time and distance are related by the factor c as by a velocity. (It should nevertheless be noticed that no physical entity is moving at velocity c; the electric field is not moving, it is merely changing in such a way that if it were visible there would appear to be waves of that velocity.)

The wave of equation 209 is *transverse* because the electric field E_y is in the y direction and the wave is propagated in the x direction.

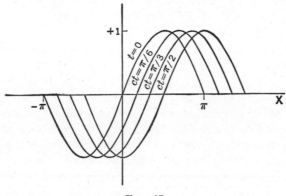

Fig. 45

Equation 206 is obtained by eliminating **H** and retaining **E** in equations 198 and 199. If the opposite procedure is followed, eliminating **E** and retaining **H**, a similar wave equation is obtained for the magnetic vector in free space:

$$\nabla^2 \mathbf{H} = \frac{1}{c^2} \frac{\partial^2 \mathbf{H}}{\partial t^2} \qquad [210]$$

The solution of this equation is a traveling wave of **H**.

It is evident that it is not possible to have an electric disturbance without having a magnetic one also, and vice versa, and it will be found that every electromagnetic wave has an electric portion and a magnetic portion traveling along together. To have one without the other would be analogous to having a water wave in which there is motion without displacement, or displacement without motion. Although there are separate wave equations for **E** and **H** they represent physically inseparable quantities.

Recognition of the fact that his electromagnetic equations had a traveling-wave solution led James Clerk Maxwell to very interesting speculations. In the first place, if it could be shown that electromagnetic waves exist, Maxwell's hypothesis relating to the ability of a displacement current to produce a magnetic field would be justified, for without that hypothesis no wave solution would result. The situation would be like a lake in which the water has weight but no mass — waves could not exist.

If electromagnetic waves do exist they should travel in free space with the velocity c, from equation 209. But c is a known quantity, a dimensional constant. It is the ratio of the electromagnetic unit of current to the electrostatic unit of current. By careful measurement of current and voltage in the laboratory, and with the aid of a balance that indicated equality of electrostatic and magnetic forces, Maxwell found (about 1865) that the numerical value of c in the metric system is a little less than 3×10^{10}. This being so, electromagnetic waves should travel, if they exist, at the rate of some 300,000 kilometers per second.

In what medium do electric waves exist? In Maxwell's time it was commonly accepted that ordinary visible light is a wave motion of a luminiferous aether, an aether pervading all space and all material, without weight but with remarkable elastic properties that permit it to propagate transverse waves. Maxwell's wave equations indicated that electromagnetic disturbances were propagated as transverse waves in some similar medium. Could it be that light is merely a form of electric wave?

Faraday had speculated upon this possibility several years earlier, and had pointed out that whereas one infinite and all-pervasive imponderable aether is a severe strain upon one's imagination, belief in two co-existent, infinite, all-pervasive, and imponderable aethers, one for light and one for electricity, is simply beyond the limits of credulity. Therefore he suspected, on this basis alone, that light is an electric phenomenon.

Maxwell had a more substantial reason for coming to the same conclusion, for he collected all the best measurements of the speed of light in vacuum, and he found that the average of those available to him was amazingly close to 300,000 kilometers per second, which was the velocity that he had predicted for electric waves from laboratory measurement of electrical units.

This being so, Maxwell's hypothesis was substantiated, and it appeared at least highly probable that light is indeed an electric wave.

Although Maxwell accepted these conclusions, many other scientists did not until Hertz, about twenty-five years later, proved the physical existence of electromagnetic waves. He accomplished this by showing their interference, reflection, and refraction. After that it was no longer possible to doubt that electromagnetic energy is propagated as wave motion. It is still safest to avoid the embarrassing question of the character of the medium in which such waves are transmitted. The best we can do is to follow Faraday's " shadow of a speculation " and " dismiss the aether but keep the vibrations."

PROBLEMS

1. Expand Maxwell's equations 198 and 199 in rectangular coordinates. By equating like components, derive from each three scalar equations (as in equation 321, page 171).

2. Prove equation 205 by expanding in Cartesian components.

3. Find the Laplacian of **H**, analogous to equation 206, but applicable to a region in which κ and μ are greater than unity. What is the velocity of an electromagnetic wave in such a region? Assume zero conductivity.

4. Extend Problem 3 by assuming the region to be conducting.

5. Prove that equation 209 is a solution of the wave equation 208. The composite function $f(x - ct)$ is differentiated according to methods discussed in calculus books.

CHAPTER X

PLANE WAVES

When light starts from a point on the sun it radiates outward in all directions and travels as a spherical wave. Part of that wave eventually reaches the earth, where we can observe it and measure it in our laboratories. The part that reaches us appears as a plane wave. That is simply because we are limited by the size of the laboratory (or at most

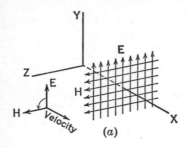

(a)

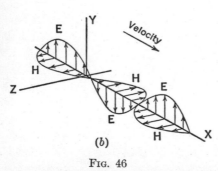

(b)

Fig. 46

by the size of the earth) and can observe only a very small part of the whole spherical wave. Just as the ocean appears flat to a man who can see only a few miles around him, so the wave appears plane to an observer who can study only a small part of it.

Much the same thing is true of radio waves. From the point of view of a transmitting antenna the wave is radiated in all directions. Indeed the radiation pattern is an important practical consideration. But, from the point of view of the receiving antenna, any wave from a station several miles away is practically a plane wave. (This statement neglects possible complications such as the effect of ground or reflections from the ionosphere.)

Let us consider a simple example of a plane wave. In Fig. 46a a cross section of a plane wave is indicated. Electric and magnetic vectors are shown in a plane parallel to the Y–Z plane. The wave is traveling from left to right along the X axis; it fills all the region shown in the figure, but only one cross section is indicated. The electric field is vertical; it is uniform throughout the plane in direction and magnitude.

ELECTRIC FIELD. We must describe this wave mathematically. First, in common with all electromagnetic waves, it must satisfy the

114

wave equation:

$$\nabla^2 \mathbf{E} = \frac{1}{c^2} \frac{\partial^2 \mathbf{E}}{\partial t^2} \qquad [206]$$

Next, because the electric field is entirely in the y direction,

$$E_x = 0 \quad E_z = 0 \qquad [211]$$

Finally, it is assumed that the electric field strength is uniform throughout the plane of the wave, and does not vary from point to point in that plane as either y or z is changed. Thus

$$\frac{\partial \mathbf{E}}{\partial y} = 0 \quad \frac{\partial \mathbf{E}}{\partial z} = 0 \qquad [212]$$

Equation 206 can be expanded into three equations representing its Cartesian components, as in equation 207, page 109. When this is done and the simplifying conditions of equations 211 and 212 are introduced the wave equation becomes merely

$$\frac{\partial^2 E_y}{\partial x^2} = \frac{1}{c^2} \frac{\partial^2 E_y}{\partial t^2} \qquad [213]$$

The solution of this equation[1] will be a mathematical expression of our wave.

The complete wave solution of equation 213 is

$$E_y = f_1(x - ct) + f_2(x + ct) \qquad [214]$$

The first part of this solution was discussed in Chapter IX and represents a wave traveling in the direction of the X axis, as in Fig. 45. The function f_1 may be any function and depends upon the type of disturbance that starts the wave. Most radio waves are approximately sinusoidal functions, and for these f_1 would be a sine or cosine function of $(x - ct)$.

The second part of the solution is also a traveling wave, but it represents a wave traveling in the *negative* x direction. Thus the complete solution describes two traveling waves,[2] one going in each direction, simultaneously passing through the same space, and the equation informs us that they travel independently of each other. For the present it will be convenient to let $f_2 = 0$. This leaves only a pure

[1] It may be noted that this is identical with equation 208, which resulted from mathematical assumptions similar to equations 211 and 212 but without any physical interpretation at the time.

[2] Other terms might be added to equation 214 as a solution of equation 213. A constant term could be added, and terms containing either x or t in the first degree, for the second derivatives of all such terms would vanish. But such terms do not represent wave action and may be disregarded in the present discussion.

traveling wave. Until we consider reflection of waves it will be unnecessary to refer to the second part of the solution.

MAGNETIC FIELD. So far only the electric component of the wave has been discussed. This must be accompanied by a magnetic component which can be determined from the electric component by means of Maxwell's equations. The general method is as follows. One of Maxwell's equations (Table III) says

$$\frac{\partial \mathbf{H}}{\partial t} = -c \, \nabla \times \mathbf{E} \qquad [215]$$

$\mathbf{E}$ is known, and its curl can be found. Thus the time derivative of $\mathbf{H}$ is determined. Integration with respect to time then gives $\mathbf{H}$.

This solution for the magnetic field can proceed to a certain extent in general terms, but it is more intelligible to consider a specific wave. It has been mentioned that the most common wave in practice is approximately sinusoidal. Let us, therefore, assume a wave in which the electric field is described by

$$E_x = 0$$
$$E_y = e_m \sin \beta(x - ct) \qquad [216]$$
$$E_z = 0$$

It will be seen that this is consistent with equation 214, for it gives the vertical component of the electric field as a function of $(x - ct)$. It is therefore a solution of the wave equation. The coefficients e_m and β can have any value; from the mathematical point of view they are merely arbitrary constants, but physically the former determines the amplitude of the wave and the latter (known as the **phase constant**) determines the frequency of its sinusoidal variation. Such a sinusoidal wave is indicated in Fig. 46b.

The first step in determining the magnetic field is to find the curl of the electric field. This is particularly simple for the wave under consideration. In general, curl is

$$\nabla \times \mathbf{E} = \begin{vmatrix} \mathbf{i} & \mathbf{j} & \mathbf{k} \\ \dfrac{\partial}{\partial x} & \dfrac{\partial}{\partial y} & \dfrac{\partial}{\partial z} \\ E_x & E_y & E_z \end{vmatrix}$$

but when the **defining conditions** of equations 211 and 212 are introduced the expression for curl becomes merely

$$\nabla \times \mathbf{E} = \mathbf{k} \, \frac{\partial E_y}{\partial x} \qquad [217]$$

and when the electric field has the value given by equation 216:

$$\nabla \times \mathbf{E} = \mathbf{k}\, e_m \beta \cos \beta(x - ct) \qquad [218]$$

Introducing this value for curl into equation 215 gives

$$\frac{\partial \mathbf{H}}{\partial t} = -\mathbf{k}\, ce_m \beta \cos \beta(x - ct) \qquad [219]$$

and by integrating we find the magnetic field to be

$$\mathbf{H} = \mathbf{k}\, e_m \sin \beta(x - ct) \qquad [220]$$

The magnetic field is thus in the direction of the Z axis and

$$H_z = e_m \sin \beta(x - ct) \qquad [221]$$

Now compare the electric and magnetic components of the wave as given by equations 216 and 221. They are identical in form and (in Gaussian units) in magnitude, but they are perpendicular in direction. This is shown in Fig. 46a and b: the electric and magnetic fields are perpendicular to each other, and both are perpendicular to the direction of travel of the wave.

Lines of electric and magnetic force are shown in Fig. 46a. Throughout the plane indicated in that figure $\mathbf{E}$ and $\mathbf{H}$ are uniform. If the plane shown in the figure is visualized as being fixed in space, $\mathbf{E}$ and $\mathbf{H}$ in that plane are constantly changing with time. If, on the other hand, the plane indicated is visualized as advancing along the Z axis with the speed of light, $\mathbf{E}$ and $\mathbf{H}$ in that plane are constant and unchanging. This is, indeed, the distinctive and defining quality of a *plane wave*.

Figure 46b is a graphical representation of the sinusoidal wave. It is traveling in the positive direction along the X axis. Vectors of $\mathbf{E}$ and $\mathbf{H}$ are shown, and each arrow represents the electric or magnetic intensity throughout the entire plane in which it lies. The length of each vector shows the strength of the field. The fields vary sinusoidally along the X axis, and when it is remembered that the entire wave train is moving along the X axis it is apparent that at any fixed point the electric and magnetic intensities vary sinusoidally with time.

Neither Fig. 46a nor 46b is a complete representation of the wave. To show the wave as it exists in three-dimensional space would require a combination of these diagrams, with the distribution of the electric and magnetic fields shown throughout many planes. Even this would be only an instantaneous picture of the wave, and would fail to show its motion; for a complete picture the imagination must be called upon to visualize what cannot be drawn upon paper.

POLARIZATION. This wave is a plane wave. It is also a polarized wave. If the electric vector oscillates as the wave passes, but maintains the same direction, the wave is said to be polarized. Mathematically, equation 211 specifies that the wave is polarized, and equations 211 and 212 together specify a polarized plane wave. In the general case of an unpolarized wave the electric and magnetic vectors change direction as well as magnitude as the wave passes. (The illustration of transverse waves traveling along a stretched rope is generally familiar: if the rope vibrates in a single plane its wave motion is polarized.)

Radio waves that arrive at a receiving antenna are usually polarized with the electric vector vertical. This is because the electric field produced by the usual radio antenna is vertical (at least near the surface of the earth). Ordinary light, on the contrary, is not polarized; but if it passes through some material that reflects, refracts, or absorbs one component of vibration while allowing the other to pass, the portion of light that is transmitted is then polarized.[3]

POWER AND THE POYNTING VECTOR. The electric and magnetic fields of a wave have now been considered; another very important aspect of wave propagation is the flow of power through space. It is apparent that a traveling wave carries energy with it, as a radio wave, for example, carries energy from the transmitter to the receiver.

As a wave passes through an imaginary surface in space, its energy will pass through that surface, and at any instant there will be a flow of power through each square centimeter of the surface. This quantity, power per unit area, which is expressed in Gaussian units as ergs per second per square centimeter, will be denoted by the symbol $\mathbf{P}$. The product $\mathbf{P} \cdot \mathbf{a}$ is power passing (at a given instant) through an area $\mathbf{a}$. $\mathbf{P}$ is a vector quantity, called the Poynting vector after a mathematician of the nineteenth century, and when flux lines of the vector field of $\mathbf{P}$ are drawn they show the flow of electromagnetic energy. The Poynting vector field is remarkably useful in electrodynamics, and the mathematical formulation of the Poynting vector is much simpler than might be expected.

Consider a region of space, enclosed within an imaginary surface. The rate at which electromagnetic energy flows out of this region is

---

[3] In optics the plane of polarization is the plane (parallel to the direction of propagation) that contains the *magnetic* vector. This definition is arbitrary and was adopted before the electromagnetic nature of light was suspected. In radio work it is not uncommon to consider the wave polarized in the direction of the *electric* vector. To avoid confusion from this inconsistency it is safer to specify polarization in terms of a given vector, as is done here.

found by integrating **P** over the enclosing surface.   Thus

$$\text{Outward flow of power} = \oint \mathbf{P} \cdot d\mathbf{a} \qquad [222]$$

But if energy is flowing out of the region, there must be a corresponding loss of electromagnetic energy stored within the region.   Electromagnetic energy is the sum of the electric and magnetic energies:

$$\text{Electric energy} = \frac{\kappa}{8\pi} \int E^2 \, dv \qquad [223]$$

$$\text{Magnetic energy} = \frac{\mu}{8\pi} \int H^2 \, dv \qquad [224]$$

$$\text{Total energy} = \frac{1}{8\pi} \int (\mu H^2 + \kappa E^2) \, dv \qquad [225]$$

The rate at which this stored energy diminishes is found by differentiation:

$$\text{Rate of decrease of stored energy} = -\frac{\partial}{\partial t} \frac{1}{8\pi} \int (\mu H^2 + \kappa E^2) \, dv \qquad [226]$$

Assuming that electrical energy is not being changed to heat by flow of current within the region, an assumption that is correct if there is zero conductivity within the region (as, for example, in free space, or in any perfect insulator), there can be a decrease of stored energy only if there is an equal outward flow of power.   Equating 222 and 226:

$$\oint \mathbf{P} \cdot d\mathbf{a} = -\frac{\partial}{\partial t} \frac{1}{8\pi} \int (\mu H^2 + \kappa E^2) \, dv \qquad [227]$$

When the indicated differentiation is performed the right-hand member becomes

$$-\frac{1}{4\pi} \int \left(\mu H \frac{\partial H}{\partial t} + \kappa E \frac{\partial E}{\partial t} \right) dv \qquad [228]$$

Since the derivatives represent the scalar rate of change of H and E, this may be written

$$-\frac{1}{4\pi} \int \left(\mu \mathbf{H} \cdot \frac{\partial \mathbf{H}}{\partial t} + \kappa \mathbf{E} \cdot \frac{\partial \mathbf{E}}{\partial t} \right) dv \qquad [229]$$

Now Maxwell's equations are used to substitute for the time derivatives, giving

$$+\frac{c}{4\pi} \int [\mathbf{H} \cdot (\nabla \times \mathbf{E}) - \mathbf{E} \cdot (\nabla \times \mathbf{H})] \, dv \qquad [230]$$

As a purely mathematical theorem, applying to any vector field, it can be shown that

$$\nabla \cdot (\mathbf{M} \times \mathbf{N}) = \mathbf{N} \cdot (\nabla \times \mathbf{M}) - \mathbf{M} \cdot (\nabla \times \mathbf{N}) \qquad [231]$$

The right-hand member of this equation corresponds exactly with the quantity in brackets in expression 230, and substitution into 230 gives

$$\frac{c}{4\pi} \int \nabla \cdot (\mathbf{E} \times \mathbf{H}) \, dv \qquad [232]$$

Divergence is here integrated through a volume, and by Gauss's theorem we may substitute for this an integration over the surface enclosing that volume. When this is done, and the result is substituted for the right-hand member of equation 227,

$$\oint \mathbf{P} \cdot d\mathbf{a} = \frac{c}{4\pi} \oint (\mathbf{E} \times \mathbf{H}) \cdot d\mathbf{a} \qquad [233]$$

Both sides of equation 233 are surface integrals, and both are integrated over the same surface enclosing an arbitrary region of space. Equation 233 is clearly satisfied if the Poynting vector is

$$\mathbf{P} = \frac{c}{4\pi} (\mathbf{E} \times \mathbf{H}) \qquad [234]$$

and thus the flow of power[4] in wave motion is obtained.

This derivation of the Poynting vector considers a region without conductivity, thereby eliminating resistance loss of energy. This is for simplicity only, and if conductivity is taken into account the result is exactly the same: equation 234 expresses the flow of electromagnetic energy in either a conducting or non-conducting region.

As a simple example of the Poynting vector field, consider a long cylindrical conductor carrying current. In Fig. 47 a steady current is flowing upward in a cylindrical conductor, the front half of the conductor being cut away in the diagram. The electric field within the conductor is correspondingly uniform and upward. The electric field outside of the conductor is much stronger, having a tangential component equal to the field within the conductor and a radial component that terminates on

---

[4] Equation 233 is equally well satisfied if there is added to 234 a function for which the integral over every closed surface is zero; a function, that is, with zero divergence. Hence, although the integral of P over a surface may commonly be taken to represent power flow, this idea may sometimes lead to absurd interpretations (i.e., if an electrostatic field and the field of a permanent magnet exist in the same region). But the integral of P over a *closed* surface is always the true outward flow of power.

some other part of the circuit.   The magnetic field within the conductor is circular, and its strength is proportional to the radius.   The Poynting field within the conductor, being **E×H**, is radially inward, growing weaker as it penetrates the conductor.

The increasing weakness of the Poynting field indicates the consumption of energy.   Energy enters the surface of the conductor and flows toward the center; it is used to supply resistance loss in the conductor,

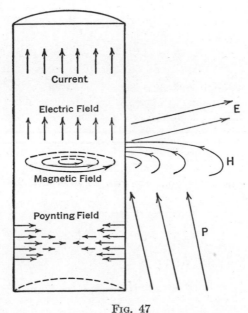

Fig. 47

and as the center of the conductor is approached the inward flow of energy decreases to zero.   This energy is supplied from the external electromagnetic field.   The Poynting field outside of the conductor is primarily parallel to the conductor, showing that energy is being carried in the direction of the conductor (to serve as a guide for energy is, indeed, the purpose of most conductors).   But the external field has a sufficient radial component to give an inward flow of energy to provide for the loss in the conductor.   Only around a conductor of perfect conductivity would the Poynting field be wholly parallel to the conductor.

Quantitatively, the electric field in such a conductor as the one in Fig. 47 is

$$\mathbf{E} = \frac{\iota}{\gamma} \tag{235}$$

from which, if the conductor radius is r, and the total current I,

$$E_z = \frac{I}{\pi r^2 \gamma} \tag{236}$$

The magnetic field at the conductor surface is, from equation 175,

$$H_\theta = \frac{2I}{cr} \tag{237}$$

Hence the Poynting field strength just within the conductor surface is

$$P_r = -\frac{c}{4\pi} \frac{2I^2}{\pi cr^3 \gamma} \tag{238}$$

where the negative sign indicates that **P** is directed radially inward. The total power entering length l of the conductor is found by multiplying P_r by the surface area $2\pi rl$:

$$\text{Entering power} = \frac{I^2 l}{\pi r^2 \gamma} \tag{239}$$

But the resistance R of the conductor is (from equation 128):

$$R = \frac{l}{\pi r^2 \gamma} \tag{240}$$

When this is substituted into equation 239 we find that the energy supplied by the Poynting field is

$$\text{Entering power} = I^2 R \tag{241}$$

This result is obviously in agreement with the well-known expression for power consumed in resistance. It is here derived by what amounts to an integration of the Poynting field to obtain flow of energy into the conductor. It illustrates a means of computing power. This method is used in a later chapter, where power radiated from a radio antenna is found by integrating the Poynting field over a surface completely surrounding the antenna.

The Poynting field of the plane wave of Fig. 46 is readily determined. From equations 216 and 221

$$\mathbf{P} = \frac{c}{4\pi} (\mathbf{E} \times \mathbf{H})$$

$$= \frac{ic}{4\pi} e_m^2 \sin^2 \beta(x - ct) \tag{242}$$

This Poynting field is everywhere in the positive x direction, a result that agrees with the obvious direction of flow of energy. It is maximum where **E** and **H** are greatest, whether they are positive or negative, and it is zero where **E** and **H** are zero.

Note particularly that the Poynting vector, and therefore the direction of travel of a wave, is boreal to the angle from **E** to **H**. If the fingers of the right hand curve from **E** to **H** the thumb shows the direction of travel of the wave. This very important relation is easily remembered if " **E×H** " is firmly impressed on the mind. Obviously a reversal of the order of these vectors would be ruinous, but the memory can be helped by noting that **E** precedes **H** as in the alphabet.

REFLECTION. When an electric wave is traveling through space there is an exact balance between the electric and magnetic fields. Half of the energy of the wave, as a matter of fact, is in the electric field and half in the magnetic. If the wave enters some different medium there must be a new distribution of energy. Whether the new medium is a dielectric material, a magnetic material, a conducting material, or an ionized region containing free charge, there will have to be a readjustment of energy relations as the wave reaches its surface. Since no energy can be added to the wave as it passes through the boundary surface, the only way that a new balance can be achieved is for some of the impinging energy to be rejected. This is what actually happens, and the rejected energy constitutes a reflected wave. Hence one sees reflection of light from a conducting metal surface and from a dielectric glass surface. Often, indeed, the transmitted wave is rapidly absorbed and lost, as when light falls upon porcelain, or wood, or gold; yet if the porcelain or wood or gold is thin enough, some of the transmitted light will pass through.

The simplest reflection to discuss is that of a plane wave falling upon a perfectly conducting plane surface. This is an extreme case, for in a perfectly conducting material the electric field strength is always zero, and it will be shown that a wave falling upon such a surface is totally reflected.

In Fig. 48 a set of coordinate axes is oriented with the Z axis downward. A perfectly conducting surface coinciding with the X–Y plane will then be horizontal. A polarized plane electromagnetic wave falling on this surface from above is defined by

$$E_{x1} = m \sin \beta(z - ct) \qquad\qquad [243]$$

The coefficient m is merely a constant; β, the phase constant, equals ω/c where ω is 2π times frequency.

But equation 243 gives the incident wave only, and when there is a reflected wave the complete solution of the wave equation must be used.

Under the circumstances described in the preceding paragraph the complete solution may be written

$$E_x = m \sin \beta(z - ct) + f_2(z + ct) \qquad [244]$$

The function indicated by f_2 is to be determined from the boundary conditions.

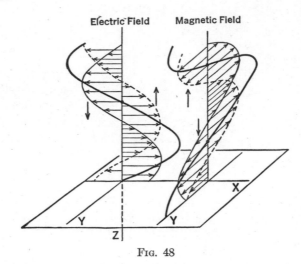

Electric Field   Magnetic Field

Fig. 48

A given boundary condition is that the plane surface is perfectly conducting and therefore at $z = 0$, $E_x = 0$. Substituting this in equation 244 gives

$$E_x = m \sin \beta(-ct) + f_2(ct) = 0 \qquad [245]$$

whence

$$f_2(ct) = -m \sin \beta(-ct) = m \sin \beta(ct) \qquad [246]$$

The complete electric field, as given by equation 244, then becomes

$$E_x = m \sin \beta(z - et) + m \sin \beta(z + ct) \qquad [247]$$

This shows that there is a reflected electric wave of the same magnitude as the incident wave, and therefore of the same energy.

The magnetic component of both waves is easily found from Maxwell's equations, as was done for a simple wave in equation 221. The result is

$$H_y = m \sin \beta(z - ct) - m \sin \beta(z + ct) \qquad [248]$$

Both electric and magnetic components are indicated in Fig. 48; each arrow indicates the field strength throughout the corresponding horizontal plane, so electric and magnetic vectors at the same height above the reflecting plane are really coincident. Note particularly that whereas the electric wave is reflected with reversal of sign, so that the electric field at the reflecting surface is always zero, the magnetic field is reflected with unchanged sign and so is doubled at the reflecting plane. The correspondence to traveling waves on transmission lines[5] is more than an analogy, for indeed the wave traveling along a transmission line is a plane electromagnetic wave and its reflection is an example of the type of reflection considered here.

Conditions in the conducting plane must be considered, to show that they are consistent with the principles of electrodynamics. The electric field in the reflecting plane must be zero. When the incident wave arrives, current flows in the plane, which can carry unlimited current with zero voltage; the current density is infinite, but its depth of penetration into the plane is zero. Magnetic intensity just above the surface is finite; just below the surface it is zero. This change takes place in zero distance, for it occurs precisely at the surface, and consequently the curl of the magnetic field *at the surface* is infinite. This is not only permissible but necessary if the current density at the surface is infinite. Study of Fig. 48 will show that the directions of current, curl, and magnetic field are in accord with Maxwell's equations.

A heavy line in Fig. 48 shows the sum of the two traveling waves. This resultant is continually changing, but it is not a traveling wave. It is oscillating in magnitude, but fixed in space: it is a " standing " wave. The total electric intensity is always zero at the reflecting surface, at a distance of one-half wavelength from the reflecting surface, and at multiples of one-half wavelength. These points are nodes. There are also nodes in the magnetic field, at one-fourth wavelength, three-fourths wavelength, and so on.

It was by detection of these nodes in front of a reflecting sheet of zinc that Hertz first proved the existence of electromagnetic waves. He explored the field with a wire loop about a foot in diameter, with the ends of the loop separated by a very minute distance; electric sparks across this small gap indicated an induced electromotive force in the loop, and the absence of sparks indicated that his loop of wire was located at a node. Since there can be nodes only if there are waves, Maxwell's theory was proved true.

The standing wave is easily expressed in mathematical form by a trigonometric change in equation 247. Reference to a table of trigonometric functions shows that this may be written

$$E_x = 2m \ (\sin \beta z)(\cos \omega t) \tag{249}$$

[5] See " Transient Electric Currents," H. H. Skilling, McGraw-Hill Book Co., N. Y., 1937.

and the resultant magnetic field can be expressed as

$$H_y = 2m \, (\cos \beta z)(\sin \omega t) \qquad [250]$$

These equations describe waves, sinusoidal along the Z axis, that are oscillating with the passage of time, but with fixed nodes where $\sin \beta z$ (or, in the latter case, $\cos \beta z$) is zero.

In a plane of finite conductivity, such as copper, conditions will closely approximate the situation here described. Some energy, but not much, will be carried by a weak transmitted wave a short distance into the copper, but most will be reflected.

The ionosphere is a region above the surface of the earth that contains a considerable density of free charge in the form of electrons. To a first approximation this may be considered a conducting region, and its reflection of radio waves (particularly long waves) is reasonably well accounted for as reflection from a conducting surface. Actually the electrons are set in motion by the incident wave and reradiate energy in a somewhat complicated manner.

PROBLEMS

1. If, in equation 216, $\beta = 1$, what are the wavelength and frequency?

2. The direction of travel of a plane wave is normal to the Z axis and midway between the X axis and the Y axis (at 45 degrees to each of the latter). The wave is polarized with the electric vector parallel to the X-Y plane. Write the necessary defining equations (similar to equations 211 and 212) and introduce them into the wave equation. Find solutions for the components of E and H, as in equation 214.

3. Prove that E and H are perpendicular in direction and identical in form and magnitude in the wave of equation 216 regardless of what function of $(x - ct)$ is assumed, and not only for a sinusoidal wave.

4. Prove that equation 231 is correct. Explain why the relation $\nabla \cdot (\mathbf{B} \times \mathbf{C}) = \mathbf{C} \cdot (\nabla \times \mathbf{B}) - \mathbf{B} \cdot (\nabla \times \mathbf{C})$ is not analogous to $\mathbf{A} \cdot (\mathbf{B} \times \mathbf{C}) = \mathbf{C} \cdot (\mathbf{A} \times \mathbf{B}) = -\mathbf{B} \cdot (\mathbf{A} \times \mathbf{C})$.

5. What is the Gaussian unit of power flow in equation 234? By what factor would the right-hand member of equation 234 be multiplied to give microwatts per square meter, with E and H remaining in Gaussian units? If P is power in watts per square meter of surface parallel to the plane of the wave, and E is volts per meter, find n in $P = nE^2$. Check your result with a radio reference book.

6. Show that in the wave of equations 216 and 221, in free space, half the energy is electric and half magnetic. Determine the electric and magnetic fields of a sinusoidal plane wave traveling in a medium in which $\kappa = 4$ and $\mu = 1$. What fraction of the total energy is in the electric field?

7. A wire is bent into a loop and the ends are attached to binding posts. A constant voltage is applied between binding posts, and current flows in the wire. Sketch the Poynting vector field about the loop of wire.

8. If the perfectly conducting surface of Fig. 48 is replaced by the surface of a non-conducting medium of dielectric constant 4 (space above the surface being vacuum), what boundary condition must be satisfied by the wave of equation 244 at the surface?

9. Find the function f_2 (equation 244) that satisfies the boundary condition of Problem 8. What is the transmitted wave? How does this relate to the reflection of light from glass? Is a radio wave partially reflected by a sheet of glass?

CHAPTER XI

RADIATION

ELECTROSTATIC POTENTIAL. In the early chapters, electrostatic potential was discussed. It was considered to be a scalar field the negative gradient of which is the electric field:

$$\mathbf{E} = -\nabla V \qquad [90]$$

The electric field may thus be found by differentiation of the potential field.

In space of unity dielectric constant the electric field is related to the electrostatic charge density by

$$\rho = \frac{1}{4\pi} \nabla \cdot \mathbf{E} \qquad [251]$$

Hence the charge density may be found from the electric field by differentiation.

Combining these equations, charge density is related directly to electrostatic potential by the Laplacian operator, which is a second-derivative operator:

$$\rho = -\frac{1}{4\pi} \nabla^2 V \qquad [252]$$

This, Poisson's equation, makes it simple to find charge density if the potential field is known.

Frequently, however, charge density is known and the electric field is desired, and one valuable property of the electrostatic potential field is that it can be computed from the distribution of charge by a relatively simple integration. The electric field can then be found as the gradient of the potential field. This gives a means of computing electric field from charge distribution, a step that cannot well be taken directly.

Similarly the magnetic field cannot readily be computed from a known current distribution but, as will be seen, the magnetic vector potential is given by an integration and the magnetic field is then found as the curl of the vector-potential field.

It was shown in Chapter IV that electrostatic potential at a given point which is r_1 units distant from the center of a spherical conductor that bears an electric charge Q_1 uniformly distributed over its surface is

$$V = \frac{Q_1}{r_1} \qquad [253]$$

If there is also a second charged sphere in the neighborhood the potential at the point under consideration will then be

$$V = \frac{Q_1}{r_1} + \frac{Q_2}{r_2} \qquad [254]$$

If there are many charged bodies the potential at a point will be the sum of the potentials resulting from each:

$$V = \sum \frac{Q}{r} \qquad [255]$$

Finally, if the charge is distributed in space with density (charge per unit volume) represented by ρ, the amount of charge in a differentially small volume dv will be $\rho\, dv$ and potential takes the form of an integral which sums the increments of potential resulting from each infinitesimal charge:

$$V = \int \frac{\rho\, dv}{r} \qquad [256]$$

Thus the expression for potential is a volume integral, the integration to be carried out through as much of the region as contains charge. This may reduce to integrating along a line, or over a surface, if the charge is limited to a line or a surface. It is clear from the derivation that r is the distance from each element of charge to the point at which the potential is being determined, a value that varies as different elements of charge are considered. In general, r is to be expressed in terms of the coordinates of the element of charge and the coordinates of the point at which potential is considered; then, if the latter coordinates are allowed to be variables, the result of the integration indicated in equation 256 will be the potential at any point (and not merely the potential at a single point), and will therefore be an expression of the potential field. Hence equation 256 gives the desired solution for the potential field in terms of charge distribution.

MAGNETIC VECTOR POTENTIAL. Chapter III introduces the idea of vector potential. The magnetic vector potential is a vector field the curl of which is the magnetic field. Thus

$$\mathbf{H} = \nabla \times \mathbf{A} \qquad [257]$$

The magnetic field is related to current density in the magnetostatic case by the familiar equation 171

$$\iota = \frac{c}{4\pi} \nabla \times \mathbf{H} \tag{258}$$

and combining these equations gives

$$\iota = \frac{c}{4\pi} \nabla \times \nabla \times \mathbf{A} = \frac{c}{4\pi} [\nabla(\nabla \cdot \mathbf{A}) - \nabla^2 \mathbf{A}] \tag{259}$$

We choose to say, in the magnetostatic case, that the divergence of **A** is zero. This is permissible, for equation 257 defines only the curl of **A** and a vector field is not defined by its curl alone. Divergence also must be known.[1] Hence we are at liberty to stipulate that there is no divergence, and it follows that

$$\iota = -\frac{c}{4\pi} \nabla^2 \mathbf{A} \tag{260}$$

The similarity of this equation 260 and equation 252 for charge density in terms of the electrostatic potential is apparent. It becomes even more obvious if the three components of equation 260 are written separately:

$$\iota_x = -\frac{c}{4\pi} \nabla^2 A_x$$

$$\iota_y = -\frac{c}{4\pi} \nabla^2 A_y \tag{261}$$

$$\iota_z = -\frac{c}{4\pi} \nabla^2 A_z$$

The solution of each of these equations is the same in form as the solution of equation 252; the solution of equation 252 is equation 256, and the parallel solution of equation 261 for A_x is

$$A_x = \frac{1}{c} \int \frac{\iota_x \, dv}{r} \tag{262}$$

Since the other two components of **A** have the same form of solution, the

---

[1] Boundary conditions as well as divergence and curl must be known for the field to be completely defined. It is here sufficient to know that the vector-potential field vanishes at infinity. There is a theorem, known as the theorem of uniqueness, which says, " A vector field is uniquely determined if the divergence and curl are specified, and if the normal component of the vector is known over a closed surface, or if the field vanishes (at least as rapidly as $1/r^2$) at infinity."

three may be combined into the single vector equation

$$\mathbf{A} = \frac{1}{c} \int \frac{\iota}{r} \, dv \qquad\qquad [263]$$

The interpretation of equation 263 is similar to that of equation 256. Vector potential is found by integrating over as much of space as may be carrying current, r being the distance from each elementary unit of current to the point at which vector potential is being determined. If current is flowing in a circuit the integration need only be performed about the circuit; elsewhere, where there is no current density, the contribution to the integral is zero. The result of the integration is the vector-potential field.

It will be seen that current flowing in the x direction produces only an x component of vector potential. In general, the direction of the vector potential is the same as that of the element of current by which it is produced. Also, the vector-potential field is strongest near the current that produces it, and fades away gradually at greater distances. The vector-potential field is sometimes described as " like the current distribution but fuzzy around the edges," or " like a picture of the current out of focus." These inelegant ideas are distinctly helpful. It is interesting to consider how they apply to the example at the end of Chapter III (page 46).

ELECTRODYNAMIC POTENTIALS. It is a great convenience to have discovered a field (the electrostatic scalar potential) which can be computed from charge distribution, and from which the electric field is readily determined; and to have another field (the magnetostatic vector potential) that may be found from current distribution and that will yield the magnetic field. But these potentials have meaning only in static situations. Equation 90 does not apply if the magnetic field is changing, and equation 258 is not valid if the electric field is changing. It is important to inquire whether in the general dynamic state it is possible to find somewhat similar potential fields that overcome this limitation.

Dynamic potentials can, indeed, be found. One is a *scalar*-potential field that, like the electrostatic potential, is determined from charge distribution. Since it reduces to the electrostatic potential field if the charge is not in motion it may be looked upon as a generalization of the electrostatic potential. The other is a *vector*-potential field that is a similar generalization of the magnetostatic vector potential and, like it, is determined by the distribution of current density.

The method of solution for determining the electrodynamic potentials is similar to that for the static potentials, the principal difference being

that equations 90 and 258, which are valid only for static fields, are
replaced by dynamic relations derived from Maxwell's equations.   Also
the assumption that the divergence of **A** equals zero is extended to fit
the dynamic situation, as will be seen.

First, we wish the curl of the vector-potential field to be the magnetic
field:

$$\mathbf{H} = \nabla \times \mathbf{A} \tag{264}$$

This defines the curl of the vector-potential field, but not its divergence,
which we are still at liberty to specify in any way we desire.

Vector potential is introduced into Maxwell's equation:

$$\nabla \times \mathbf{E} = -\frac{1}{c}\frac{\partial \mathbf{H}}{\partial t} = -\frac{1}{c}\nabla \times \frac{\partial \mathbf{A}}{\partial t} \tag{265}$$

It is clear that this relation is satisfied by

$$\mathbf{E} = -\frac{1}{c}\frac{\partial \mathbf{A}}{\partial t} \tag{266}$$

but it is also satisfied if

$$\mathbf{E} = -\frac{1}{c}\frac{\partial \mathbf{A}}{\partial t} - \nabla V \tag{267}$$

That equation 267 satisfies equation 265 may be seen by taking the curl
of both sides; since the curl of the gradient of any scalar field V is
identically zero, equation 267 is justified.   Equation 267 is a more
general form of equation 90, applicable to fields that are changing as
well as to those that are static.

Equation 267 (instead of equation 90) is now substituted into equation
251, giving

$$\rho = \frac{1}{4\pi}\nabla \cdot \mathbf{E} = -\frac{1}{4\pi}\left[\frac{1}{c}\frac{\partial}{\partial t}\nabla \cdot \mathbf{A} + \nabla^2 V\right] \tag{268}$$

The resulting equation 268 cannot be solved while it contains both **A**
and V.   But it contains **A** only as the divergence, and we are still free
to specify the divergence of **A** in any way we wish.   Let us take advantage of this opportunity to specify $\nabla \cdot \mathbf{A}$ in terms of V and make

$$\nabla \cdot \mathbf{A} = -\frac{1}{c}\frac{\partial V}{\partial t} \tag{269}$$

This is an arbitrarily assumed relation, but it turns out to be a singularly
useful one, for it is now possible to write, from equation 268,

$$\rho = -\frac{1}{4\pi}\left(\nabla^2 V - \frac{1}{c^2}\frac{\partial^2 V}{\partial t^2}\right) \tag{270}$$

The analogy between this and the electrostatic equation 252 is obvious, and this may be considered the dynamic form of Poisson's equation (with $\kappa = 1$).

In finding the dynamic vector potential equation 258 is not adequate, but from Maxwell's equations we find the more general form to be (with $\mu = 1$):

$$\iota = \frac{c}{4\pi}\left(\nabla\times\mathbf{H} - \frac{1}{c}\frac{\partial\mathbf{E}}{\partial t}\right) \tag{271}$$

Since $\mathbf{H}$ is the curl of the vector potential, and since $\mathbf{E}$ can be expressed in terms of the vector and scalar potentials by means of equation 267,

$$\iota = \frac{c}{4\pi}\left[\nabla\times\nabla\times\mathbf{A} + \frac{1}{c^2}\frac{\partial^2\mathbf{A}}{\partial t^2} + \nabla\left(\frac{1}{c}\frac{\partial V}{\partial t}\right)\right] \tag{272}$$

The full value of the assumption of equation 269 now becomes apparent, for not only was it used to eliminate $\mathbf{A}$ from equation 270, but also it will serve to eliminate V from equation 272. When this is done, and when the curl of the curl of $\mathbf{A}$ is expanded according to equation 205, there results the dynamic form of equation 260:

$$\iota = \frac{c}{4\pi}\left[\nabla(\nabla\cdot\mathbf{A}) - \nabla^2\mathbf{A} + \frac{1}{c^2}\frac{\partial^2\mathbf{A}}{\partial t^2} - \nabla(\nabla\cdot\mathbf{A})\right]$$

$$= -\frac{c}{4\pi}\left(\nabla^2\mathbf{A} - \frac{1}{c^2}\frac{\partial^2\mathbf{A}}{\partial t^2}\right) \tag{273}$$

Solutions for the static potentials were found in integral form. Equations 270 and 273 for the dynamic potentials are similar to equations 252 and 260 for the static, except that each contains a time derivative, and solutions of these dynamic equations can also be expressed as integrals. They are

$$V = \int \frac{\rho\left(t - \dfrac{r}{c}\right)}{r}\, dv \tag{274}$$

$$\mathbf{A} = \frac{1}{c}\int \frac{\iota\left(t - \dfrac{r}{c}\right)}{r}\, dv \tag{275}$$

Proof that equation 274 gives the correct dynamic scalar potential is obtained by substituting it into equation 270, which is thereby[2] reduced

---

[2] The substitution of V from equation 274 into equation 270 is not entirely straightforward, however. Direct substitution of equation 274 into equation 270

to an identity. And since equation 274 is a solution of equation 270 it follows that the similar equation 275 is a solution of equation 273.

The meaning of equation 274 is this: the element of charge $\rho\, dv$ contributes to the scalar potential at every point in space but in a manner involving a time delay. The charge density at any particular point is a function of time, written $\rho(t)$. The effect that this charge has on the potential at some other point is determined by the same function of a smaller value of time, written $\rho\left(t - \dfrac{r}{c}\right)$ — a function of a value of time that is less than t by r/c. In other words, the effect that the charge $\rho\, dv$ has on the potential of a point at time t is determined not by the value of $\rho\, dv$ at time t, but by the value of $\rho\, dv$ at the earlier time $t - r/c$. Since r is the distance from the charge producing the potential to the point at which the potential is measured, it appears that c is a velocity. It is the speed at which a change of potential is conveyed through space. It is, of course, the speed of light.

The interpretation of equation 275 is similar. Vector potential at a point is determined by the current flowing at some other point *at a slightly earlier time*. Because V and $\mathbf{A}$ are potentials that appear in space at times later than the charges and currents that produce them, they are called *retarded potentials*.

If changes of electric and magnetic fields take place slowly the retarded potentials are indistinguishable from the electrostatic scalar potential and the magnetostatic vector potential; this is true also when the fields are observed at points close to the source of the disturbance, for then the time lag is negligibly small. Mathematically,

---

leads to difficulty in determining the Laplacian of ρ/r at points at which r may be zero. Since r is the distance from an element of charge to the point at which potential is being determined, it can be zero only when potential is being determined at a point at which charge is located. To avoid the difficulty, space is divided into two regions: one so close to the point at which potential is being determined that quasi-stationary conditions apply and $\nabla^2 V = -4\pi\rho$; the other containing all the rest of space. For the second region ρ/r is regular and the Laplacian of V is readily expanded in spherical coordinates to obtain

$$\int \frac{1}{r} \frac{\partial^2}{\partial r^2} \rho\left(t - \frac{r}{c}\right) dv$$

Since both regions contribute to the potential at the point in question, the complete expression to be substituted for the Laplacian in equation 270 is

$$\nabla^2 V = -4\pi\rho + \int \frac{1}{r} \frac{\partial^2}{\partial r^2} \rho\left(t - \frac{r}{c}\right) dv$$

Thereafter the solution proceeds without trouble and equation 270 reduces to an identity. See, for example, Abraham and Becker's " Classical Electricity and Magnetism."

if r is small compared to ct, a function of $(t - r/c)$ is negligibly different from a function of t. When times are long and distances short the equations of static fields can be used quite satisfactorily even though fields are slowly changing; this is the **quasi-stationary state**. All problems at power frequencies are quasi-stationary except those that deal with long transmission lines. The time delay in the propagation of a magnetic field within a generator, for instance, is negligible.

RADIATION. The electrical phenomenon that is most essentially a dynamic problem is radiation of waves from an antenna. If a radio antenna were considered from the quasi-stationary point of view there would be no suggestion of radiation of energy, for radiation is the factor that the quasi-stationary solution overlooks. So to determine radiation from an antenna we will seek a solution for the dynamic vector potential as given by equation 275. That is the purpose for which the concepts of vector potential and retarded potential have been introduced.

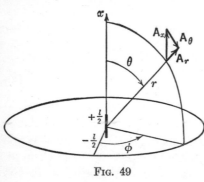

FIG. 49

Let us consider a short length of wire carrying alternating current:

$$i = I \sin \omega t \qquad [276]$$

The wire is isolated in space (there is no ground surface near). Its length is l, and we will locate a set of spherical coordinates in such a way that the conductor extends along the polar axis from $-l/2$ to $+l/2$; see Fig. 49. Using equation 275 it is simple to write the vector potential about this short wire, for the integration need only be performed along the wire, in the direction we may call x, from one end of the wire to the other, as follows:

$$A_x = \frac{1}{c} \int_{-l/2}^{l/2} \frac{I \sin \omega \left(t - \dfrac{r}{c} \right)}{r}\, dx \qquad [277]$$

Since current is in the x direction only, there is only an x component of vector potential.

Now if the length of the wire is small compared to the distance at which **A** is measured, the denominator of the integrand is practically constant during the course of integration. If the length is small compared with the wavelength of the radiated signal, the numerator is also practically constant; this means that at any point in space the phase of a signal from one end of the radiating wire is negligibly different from the phase of the signal arriving at the same point from the other end of the wire.   With these assumptions the integrand of equation 277 is merely a constant and

$$A_x = \frac{Il}{cr} \sin \omega \left(t - \frac{r}{c} \right)$$ [278]

Thus simply is the vector-potential field found from the known current.

To find the magnetic field about the short antenna the curl of the vector potential is determined.   This may best be done in spherical coordinates, using the formula of Table II..   Vector potential is readily changed to spherical components, as illustrated in Fig. 49, giving

$$A_r = \frac{Il}{cr} \sin \omega \left(t - \frac{r}{c} \right) \cos \theta$$

$$A_\theta = - \frac{Il}{cr} \sin \omega \left(t - \frac{r}{c} \right) \sin \theta$$ [279]

$$A_\phi = 0$$

Taking the curl gives, in accordance with equation 257, the magnetic field:

$$H_r = 0$$
$$H_\theta = 0$$ [280]
$$H_\phi = \frac{Il}{cr} \sin \theta \left[\frac{\omega}{c} \cos \omega \left(t - \frac{r}{c} \right) + \frac{1}{r} \sin \omega \left(t - \frac{r}{c} \right) \right]$$

The electric field can be found from the magnetic field by Maxwell's equation, equation 271, or from the vector potential by equation 267. To illustrate the latter method we must first find the scalar potential V from equation 269

$$V = -c\nabla \cdot \int \mathbf{A} \; dt$$ [281]

When this[3] is substituted into equation 267 there results an expression

[3] Equation 281 may be written $V = -\nabla \cdot \mathbf{Z}$ where

$$\mathbf{Z} = c \int \mathbf{A} \, dt$$

This **Z** is the **Hertzian vector** (which exists generally, although this definition applies only in free space).   The Hertzian field is particularly interesting because it is sufficient by itself to describe all electromagnetic action; when the Hertzian field is known **A**, V, **H** and **E**, ρ and i may all be computed from it.   In other words, every electric or magnetic phenomenon may be looked upon as merely a change in the Hertzian field.   This does away with the duality of the electric and magnetic fields, and substitutes the concept of a unitary Hertzian field to comprise all electromagnetic action.

entirely in **A**:

$$\mathbf{E} = -\frac{1}{c}\frac{\partial \mathbf{A}}{\partial t} + c\nabla \nabla \cdot \int \mathbf{A}\ dt \qquad [282]$$

This somewhat disturbing array of symbols indicates operations that are easily carried out one at a time, giving

$$E_r = \frac{2Il}{\omega r}\cos\theta\left[\frac{\omega}{cr}\sin\omega\left(t - \frac{r}{c}\right) - \frac{1}{r^2}\cos\omega\left(t - \frac{r}{c}\right)\right]$$

$$E_\theta = \frac{Il}{\omega r}\sin\theta\left[\frac{\omega^2}{c^2}\cos\omega\left(t - \frac{r}{c}\right) + \frac{\omega}{rc}\sin\omega\left(t - \frac{r}{c}\right) - \frac{1}{r^2}\cos\omega\left(t - \frac{r}{c}\right)\right] \quad [283]$$

$$E_\phi = 0$$

It is easier to discover the physical meaning of equations 280 and 283 if they are expressed in terms of wavelength λ and frequency f, using the following relations:

$$\lambda = \frac{c}{f} = \frac{2\pi c}{\omega} \qquad [284]$$

They may then be written:

$$H_r = 0$$

$$H_\theta = 0$$

$$H_\phi = \frac{\omega Il\ \sin\theta}{rc^2}\left[-\frac{1}{2\pi}\frac{\lambda}{r}\sin\left(2\pi\frac{r}{\lambda} - \omega t\right) + \cos\left(2\pi\frac{r}{\lambda} - \omega t\right)\right] \qquad [285]$$

$$E_r = -\frac{2\omega Il\cos\theta}{rc^2}\left[\frac{1}{4\pi^2}\frac{\lambda^2}{r^2}\cos\left(2\pi\frac{r}{\lambda} - \omega t\right) + \frac{1}{2\pi}\frac{\lambda}{r}\sin\left(2\pi\frac{r}{\lambda} - \omega t\right)\right]$$

$$E_\theta = \frac{\omega Il\sin\theta}{rc^2}\left[-\frac{1}{4\pi^2}\frac{\lambda^2}{r^2}\cos\left(2\pi\frac{r}{\lambda} - \omega t\right) - \frac{1}{2\pi}\frac{\lambda}{r}\sin\left(2\pi\frac{r}{\lambda} - \omega t\right)\right. \qquad [286]$$

$$\left. + \cos\left(2\pi\frac{r}{\lambda} - \omega t\right)\right]$$

$$E_\phi = 0$$

Let us consider these equations in two general regions: first, near the radiating wire, in the region where r is small compared to the wavelength λ, and second, at a distance of several wavelengths so that r is large compared to λ. In the region near the antenna the terms containing λ/r in the highest degree predominate. Quite close to the antenna we may disregard all terms except the first in each bracket in equations 285 and 286, and when this is done the equations reduce to the quasi-stationary equations of an oscillating doublet.[4]   A short wire carrying alternating current from end to end is, in fact, a good physical representation of an oscillating doublet, which is best visualized by considering that the short wire is connected between two metal spheres; the spheres act as a condenser, and the current carried by the wire alternately charges and discharges their capacitance.   The electric field from sphere to sphere and the magnetic field about the wire are described (in the appropriate region) by the first terms of equations 285 and 286.   The appropriate region is that in which the observer is far enough from the antenna so that it looks like a doublet, yet at a distance that is short compared to the wavelength λ.

If, on the other hand, the field is observed at a distance of many wavelengths from the source, so that λ/r is small, another interesting and important simplification appears.   In this case terms containing λ/r and λ^2/r^2 are so small that they may be neglected.   Only the last term need be retained in the expression for E_θ, and the entire expression for E_r is negligible compared to E_θ.   Also, only the last term for H_ϕ is significant.   With these approximations, which are good at a distance of several wavelengths from the origin, the wave equations become

$$E_r = 0$$
$$E_\theta = \frac{\omega I l \sin \theta}{r c^2} \cos \left(2\pi \frac{r}{\lambda} - \omega t \right) \qquad [287]$$
$$E_\phi = 0$$
$$H_r = 0$$
$$H_\theta = 0 \qquad [288]$$
$$H_\phi = \frac{\omega I l \sin \theta}{r c^2} \cos \left(2\pi \frac{r}{\lambda} - \omega t \right)$$

These equations 287 and 288 describe a beautifully simple electromagnetic field.   It is a wave traveling radially outward.   The electric and magnetic components are identical in magnitude and in form and are mutually perpendicular.   The electric and magnetic components become weaker as the wave travels outward because both are inversely proportional to the radius.   The Poynting vector that describes the flow of energy is radially outward and is inversely proportional to the square of the radius; this shows that there is no loss of energy, and that the energy density merely diminishes as the wave spreads.

[4] A doublet or dipole results when a particle with positive charge and a particle with equal negative charge are very close together (compared with the distance from which they are observed).   An oscillating doublet is one in which the charge on each particle varies sinusoidally with time.

Figure 50 shows the appearance of one section of the wave. It is a spherical wave. Lines of the magnetic field are parallels of latitude on the sphere, and the electric field is along meridians. Both fields are strongest near the equator, and vanish at the poles. The fields at any fixed point in space are, of course, oscillating sinusoidally.

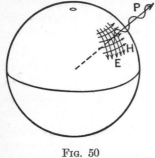

FIG. 50

Any small portion of the spherical traveling wave cannot be distinguished from a plane wave. The similarity of Fig. 50 to Fig. 46a is obvious. In equations 287 and 288 the term cos $(2\pi r/\lambda - \omega t)$ may be considered to define a plane wave, and the coefficient of that term is interpreted as giving the strength of the wave in different parts of space. This is an approximation based upon the fact that if only a small portion of the wave is observed, neither sin θ in the numerator nor r in the denominator of the coefficient can change appreciably in the region under observation. Derivatives of the coefficient will therefore be vanishingly small. It is for this reason that a received radio wave can usually be considered a plane wave.

There is a great deal of information in equations 285 and 286, the complete expressions for the spherical wave, that has not been considered. A few of the more obvious points are as follows.

Near the source of the waves the electric and magnetic fields are out of phase in time. The magnetic field near the antenna is in phase with the antenna current, whereas the electric field is in phase with the charge on either end of the antenna. These components that predominate near the antenna are called the **induction** components of the field. The induction components of the electric and magnetic fields contain a relatively large amount of energy that is alternating between the electric and the magnetic fields in the immediate vicinity of the apparatus, whatever it may be. The magnetic field in a transformer or a generator, for instance, is almost exclusively the induction field.

But the induction component is negligibly small at a distance of several wavelengths from the source, for it diminishes with the square or cube of the radius, while another component that diminishes only as the first power of the radius becomes predominant. This latter component is known as the **radiation** component. The radiation component represents energy that is traveling outward and that never returns to the circuit from which it was sent. It is a component that appears only in the complete electrodynamic equations, and that is omitted from quasi-stationary expressions for the fields. The radiation components of electric and magnetic fields are in phase with each other. The induction and radiation components of the electric field, in the region where both exist, are in phase opposition, while those of the magnetic field are in phase quadrature; this unexpected result may be explained by considering that the radiation component does not originate directly from current and charge in the antenna, but rather from the changes of the induction fields surrounding the antenna.

The induction and radiation terms of both the electric and magnetic fields are equal in magnitude when $\lambda/r = 2\pi$, or at a radius from the origin of approximately one-sixth of a wavelength. Beyond that radius the radiation component becomes predominant in proportion to the distance. Hence it may be concluded that phenomena taking place at distances less than one-sixth of a wavelength from a short antenna are predominantly inductive, and that those at greater distances are predominantly the result of radiation. Thus many of the early demonstrations of " wireless telegraphy " were primarily the result of induction.

The distinction between the induction and the radiation terms of equations 285 and 286 is a mathematical one: terms containing certain powers of r are induction, those with other powers of r are radiation. But another distinction is more open to physical interpretation, as follows.

In the quasi-stationary state there are electric and magnetic fields that are changing slowly. Their configuration at any instant is that of electrostatic or magnetostatic fields, for their rate of change is so slow that they have no mutual effect upon each other. The quasi-stationary electric field emanates from near-by electric charge, and the quasi-stationary magnetic field encircles an electric current. These are *induction* fields; there is no radiation.

The dynamic state differs from the quasi-stationary state because it takes into account the ability of a changing electric field to induce a magnetic field, and of a changing magnetic field to induce an electric field. Radiation is the result. The radiation components of the electric and magnetic fields have no such close relation to charge and current as have the induction fields. They are cut adrift from their source. The electric field of a wave results not from the near-by presence of charge, but from a changing magnetic component in the wave; the magnetic field does not result from an actual flow of current, but from a changing electric field. Neither, of course, could have originated if there had not somewhere been a charge and a current, but they may travel any distance and propagate each other for an unlimited time. Consider, for example, the light waves from an extra-galactic nova that reach us millions of years after the brilliance that created them has ceased and the star become extinct.

PROBLEMS

1. A short, straight piece of wire of length l is carrying current $i = I \sin \omega t$. Using equation 262, show that the magnetic vector potential resulting from the current in this piece of wire, at distances from the wire that are great compared to the length of the wire, is $\dfrac{Il \sin \omega t}{cr}$. Indicate the vector-potential field graphically.

2. Find the magnetic field about the short piece of wire of Problem 1 by determining the curl of the vector-potential field. Show that it is equal to the quasi-stationary term of equation 280.

3. Show that the quasi-stationary terms of equation 283 result from a solution for electric potential about an oscillating dipole in the region in which equation 254 can be used. (Note: The solution is greatly simplified by making use of the fact that the length of the dipole, which may be called l, is small compared to the distance r from the midpoint of the dipole to the point at which the potential and electric field are computed. Thus $r^2 - l^2$ is approximately r^2. Also it is permissible to let $r_1 = r - (l/2) \cos \theta$ and $r_2 = r + (l/2) \cos \theta$).

4. Show that equation 270 has also an *advanced* *potential* solution $V = \displaystyle\int \dfrac{\rho\left(t + \dfrac{r}{c}\right)}{r}\, dv$ as well as the retarded potential solution of equation 274. What is the physical meaning of this " advanced potential "?

5. A spherical condenser consisting of a metal ball surrounded by a concentric metal shell is discharged by making an electrical connection between the inner and outer spheres. The discharge is oscillatory. Is there radiation? Explain.

CHAPTER XII

ANTENNAS

SHORT ANTENNAS. A short vertical antenna above a ground surface of good conductivity radiates essentially according to the equations of Chapter XI. It must be short compared to the radiated wavelength, since that was a necessary condition in integrating equation 277.

The effect of the ground surface can be taken into account ·by a common artifice in which the conducting surface is looked upon as a mirror to reflect electric waves. Consider first a vertical wire that is quite remote from ground or any other interfering object. Current is made to oscillate from end to end of the wire, charging the capacitance between the upper and lower ends. The resulting electric and magnetic fields are symmetrical with respect to a horizontal plane through the midpoint of the wire. (The apparatus itself need not be a single straight wire; it may take any shape provided it is symmetrical above and below a horizontal plane. There will then be symmetry in the electric and magnetic fields.) Now consider that the imaginary bisecting plane is made a very thin sheet of perfectly conducting material. Nothing will be altered. This surface is everywhere perpendicular to the electric field and will not distort it. Current will flow in the sheet, but merely to maintain the fields in their original configuration, and since the sheet is perfectly conducting there will be no loss of energy.

With such a conducting sheet in place, the electric and magnetic fields of the upper half of the wire will be completely independent of those about the lower half. Indeed the lower half of the wire, and its fields — everything below the plane of symmetry — may be completely eliminated, and above the surface the electric and magnetic fields and the radiation pattern will remain unchanged.

The reverse of this process is the means of solution to be used for an antenna above a perfect ground: the actual antenna and conducting plane can be replaced by an isolated antenna of double length, and the electromagnetic field will be the same. This method, indeed, was used in the previous chapter for a short vertical antenna, but with the above considerations of symmetry it can be applied more generally: the effect of an antenna-and-conducting-plane is the same (above the plane) as the antenna-and-its-mirror-image-as-seen-reflected-in-the-plane (the plane itself being removed) if currents and charges in the image are equal and opposite to those in the antenna.

If the antenna is a single vertical wire above ground it will obviously have no current at its upper end. Current will be maximum at the bottom and in a short antenna it will decrease, very nearly in proportion to the height, to zero at the top. This is a common type of practical antenna. Another common type has a vertical wire leading up to an array of horizontal wires. In this case the horizontal wires may provide enough capacitance to ground so that the current in the vertical lead is essentially uniform from top to bottom. Radiation from the vertical wire is then found by using the equations of the previous chapter which were developed for a wire with uniform current distribution. The primary purpose of the horizontal wires of such a " flat-top " antenna is to provide capacitance, to increase current in the vertical wire, and thereby to increase radiation from it. There is some radiation from the horizontal wires also, but that is incidental and may usually be neglected. It is assumed in this discussion that all dimensions of the antenna are small compared with the radiated wavelength; equations 287 and 288 are then directly applicable to a vertical antenna with large capacitance at the top if twice the height above ground is used for l in those equations.

When the antenna is a single vertical wire, with current varying from maximum at the bottom to zero at the top, the effective height is less than the actual height. If the antenna is quite short the effective height is half the actual height, for radiation is proportional to the average current which is half the current at the base. If the antenna approaches a quarter-wavelength in height the current distribution can no longer be considered linear, and the effective height is somewhat greater than half the actual height. To be sure, the derivations of Chapter XI exclude antennas of such length, but as will be seen, the error in the result is not more than a few per cent if the proper equivalent height is used, and equations 287 and 288 are applicable to a simple vertical antenna if l is taken to be twice the actual height above ground multiplied by an appropriate factor that varies from 0.5 for a short antenna to 0.6 (more exactly, $2/\pi$) for a quarter-wavelength antenna.

RADIATED POWER. The total power radiated from an antenna is often of interest. When only the radiation component is considered, the Poynting vector is radial and, since it is in the direction of $\mathbf{E} \times \mathbf{H}$, it is outward. The total energy transported by the traveling wave of radiation is found by integrating the Poynting vector over an imaginary spherical surface with its center at the origin. Because of the symmetry of the spherical wave of Chapter XI this is an easy integration and gives

$$\int \mathbf{P} \cdot d\mathbf{a} = \int \frac{c}{4\pi} (\mathbf{E} \times \mathbf{H}) \cdot d\mathbf{a}$$

$$= \int \frac{c}{4\pi} \left[\frac{\omega I l}{rc^2} \sin \theta \cos \left(2\pi \frac{r}{\lambda} - \omega t\right) \right]^2 (2\pi r^2 \sin \theta) \, d\theta$$

$$= \frac{\omega^2 I^2 l^2 \cos^2 \left(2\pi \dfrac{r}{\lambda} - \omega t\right)}{2c^3} \int_0^\pi \sin^3 \theta \, d\theta$$

$$= \frac{2\omega^2 I^2 l^2}{3c^3} \cos^2 \left(2\pi \frac{r}{\lambda} - \omega t\right) \qquad \text{[289]}$$

The Poynting vector is a function of time, varying as the square of the cosine. For most purposes the average power of the radiated wave is desired, and since the average value of the cosine squared function is $\frac{1}{2}$, it follows that the average power radiated from a short isolated antenna with uniform current distribution is

$$\text{Average power} = \frac{\omega^2 I^2 l^2}{3c^3} \qquad \text{[290]}$$

RADIATION RESISTANCE. A term that is defined as the radiated power divided by the square of the effective value of current in the antenna lead is called **radiation resistance.** In equation 290, I is the *maximum* value of current; the square of the *effective* current is $\frac{1}{2}I^2$, so the radiation resistance of a short antenna is

$$\frac{2}{3} \frac{\omega^2 l^2}{c^3} \qquad \text{[291]}$$

Expression 291 is in statohms, the Gaussian unit. Since, from Table I, 1 statohm $= c^2 \cdot 10^{-9}$ ohms, or about $30c$ ohms, the radiation resistance can be written

$$20 \frac{\omega^2 l^2}{c^2} \text{ ohms} \qquad \text{[292]}$$

This formula applies to an isolated wire of length l in which the current distribution is uniform. The radiation resistance of a short antenna above ground is found by making l twice the effective height of the antenna. The resulting value of radiation resistance is then divided by two because, since there is radiation into only half of space, only half as much power is to be represented by the radiation resistance of an antenna above ground. Thus for a grounded antenna of *equivalent* height h_e

$$\text{Radiation resistance} = 40\,\frac{\omega^2 h_e^2}{c^2} = 1600\,\frac{h_e^2}{\lambda^2} \qquad [293]$$

The derivation of this expression for radiation resistance is limited to an antenna that is short in comparison with the radiated wavelength, but in fact it is a good approximation if the height does not exceed a quarter-wavelength when the proper equivalent height is used.

OTHER EXPRESSIONS FOR RADIATION. The equations of the radiated wave are given in equations 287 and 288 in terms of antenna current. For many purposes it is more interesting to express the wave as a function of the antenna voltage and capacitance. I is the amplitude of the current, and if V is the amplitude of the voltage and C the capacitance of the isolated antenna from end to end, so that $I = \omega C V$, the components that comprise the wave of radiation are

$$E_\theta = \frac{\omega^2 V C l \sin\theta}{r c^2}\cos\left(2\pi\,\frac{r}{\lambda} - \omega t\right) \qquad [294]$$

$$H_\phi = \frac{\omega^2 V C l \sin\theta}{r c^2}\cos\left(2\pi\,\frac{r}{\lambda} - \omega t\right) \qquad [295]$$

When applied to a grounded antenna V is twice the voltage to ground, C is half the capacitance to ground, and l is twice the equivalent height of the antenna. From these equations it appears that an increased signal strength is obtained by increasing the height of an antenna, or its capacitance, or the voltage applied to it, or the frequency of the oscillation. In free space, the field strength resulting from constant antenna voltage is proportional to the square of the frequency. The radiated energy therefore increases with the fourth power of the frequency.

It is often desirable to have the radiation field and particularly the electric component in practical units. The necessary changes from the Gaussian units of equation 287 are easily made, giving

$$E_\theta = \frac{\pi f l I}{5r}\sin\theta\cos\left(\omega t - \frac{2\pi r}{\lambda}\right)\ \text{microvolts per meter} \qquad [296]$$

This is for the electric field strength at a distance r meters from an isolated short antenna that carries current I amperes throughout its length of l meters; t is time in seconds, f is the frequency of the current in cycles per second, $\omega = 2\pi f$, and λ is the radiated wavelength in meters. The angle θ is the angle that a radial line from the antenna to the point of observation makes with vertical.

This equation can be used for a simple antenna *above ground* if l is twice the effective height of the antenna and I the current at the base of the antenna.

Commonly the effective or r.m.s. value of electric field strength is all that is desired. For this purpose only the coefficient of equation 296 is needed, and if I is the effective or r.m.s. value of antenna current

$$E_\theta = \frac{\pi f l I}{5r} \sin \theta \text{ r.m.s. microvolts per meter} \qquad [297]$$

RADIATION PATTERN. It is quite common to show the "radiation pattern" of an antenna by plotting vectors radially from a point, the length of each vector being proportional to the field strength encountered at a given distance in the indicated direction. If, for example, the field were stronger to the north than to the south, the vector to the north would be the longer. A curve connecting the ends of the vectors is then the radiation pattern. The field strength is frequently plotted in micro-volts per meter at a distance of 1 mile.

The radiation pattern in a horizontal plane of a short vertical antenna is plotted in Fig. 51a. Since radiation is equal in all horizontal directions, all radial vectors are equal, and the pattern is merely a circle.

The radiation pattern of the short vertical antenna in a vertical plane is shown in Fig. 51b. The maximum radiation is horizontal, and vertical radiation is zero. Radiation in any other

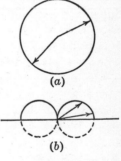

(a)

(b)

FIG. 51

direction is proportional to the sine of the angle between that direction and the vertical, as in equation 296, so the pattern is composed of a pair of circles as shown.

LONGER ANTENNAS. When the length of an antenna is considerable compared with a wavelength, it can no longer be considered a short antenna. (With 10-centimeter waves, a 2-inch antenna is "long.") It may then be treated as a number of short sections in series. Each differential length of the antenna radiates a spherical wave, and the output of the entire antenna is obtained by integration, with due regard for different magnitude and phase of current in the different elements.

The method is best illustrated by an example. Consider a simple vertical antenna, composed of a single perfect conductor. It is erected above a perfectly conducting ground surface, and fed at its base with a sine wave of voltage of such frequency that the height of the antenna is one-quarter wavelength.

There are two points to consider before starting the analysis. First, the perfectly conducting ground plane acts as a mirror, so that an observer anywhere above the ground surface receives the same signal from an antenna of length l above a perfectly conducting plane that he would receive from an antenna of length $2l$ that was isolated in space and fed in the middle. It is convenient to substitute for the antenna-and-ground-plane, in which the flow of current and distribution of charge are quite complicated, the relatively simple antenna-and-image combination. Thus we will consider an antenna excited in the middle and extending one-quarter wavelength in each direction. The total power radiated from such an antenna will be twice that from the actual quarter-wave antenna, but the distribution of energy in the hemisphere of space above the ground surface will be the same. With the actual antenna and ground there will, of course, be no energy in the hemisphere below the ground surface.

Second, a rigorous solution for current distribution in a simple vertical antenna is exceedingly difficult. At the top of the antenna there can be no current, while at the bottom the current has some definite value. It is usual to assume that the distribution of current is similar to that on an open-circuited transmission line, being proportional to the sine of the distance from the top. Thus a quarter-wavelength antenna would have maximum current at the base and if this is called I_0 the current at any height x is

$$i = I_0 \cos \frac{2\pi x}{\lambda} \sin \omega t \qquad [298]$$

The wavelength of the radiated signal is λ.

The method of solution is to find the electric field produced by each short length of the antenna and combine them (by integration) into the total field. Thus a short section of the antenna of differential length dx, located at a height x, will carry a current given by equation 298 and will produce a radiation field given by equation 287. Combining these equations, and integrating for values of x between the limits $-\lambda/4$ and $\lambda/4$, thereby including both antenna and image, the electric field produced by a quarter-wave antenna is

$$E_\theta = \int_{-\lambda/4}^{\lambda/4} \frac{\omega I_0 \cos \frac{2\pi x}{\lambda} \sin \theta}{r_e c^2} \cos \omega \left(t - \frac{r_e}{c} \right) dx \qquad [299]$$

In this equation r_e is used to represent the distance from the current-carrying element to the point at which field strength is being measured, which must be distinguished from r, the distance from the origin of the coordinate system assumed to be at the base of the antenna. Since we are interested in the electric field at distances from the antenna greater than several wavelengths, the difference between r_e and r in the denominator of the integrand is negligible. But in the cosine term the difference between r_e and r is essential, for it is this difference that determines the phase relation of radiation from different parts of the antenna. In the denominator it is quite satisfactory to substitute r for r_e, but in the phase relation it is necessary to use an approximation that cannot be in error by more than a small fraction of a wavelength:

$$r_e = r - x \cos \theta \qquad [300]$$

Also the angle between r_e and the vertical antenna is practically θ. With these changes,

$$E_\theta = \frac{\omega I_0 \sin \theta}{rc^2} \int_{-\lambda/4}^{\lambda/4} \cos \frac{2\pi x}{\lambda} \cos \omega \left(t - \frac{r}{c} + \frac{x \cos \theta}{c} \right) dx \qquad [301]$$

Performance of this integration, although somewhat involved, is essentially simple. The result is

$$E_\theta = \frac{2I_0}{rc} \cos \omega' \left(t - \frac{r}{c} \right) \frac{\cos \left(\frac{\pi}{2} \cos \theta \right)}{\sin \theta} \qquad [302]$$

The other components of the electric field are of course zero, as they are for a short antenna. The magnetic field is perpendicular to the electric field (as it is for each elementary length of antenna) and, in Gaussian units, is equal to it. Hence

$$H_\phi = \frac{2I_0}{rc} \cos \omega \left(t - \frac{r}{c} \right) \frac{\cos \left(\frac{\pi}{2} \cos \theta \right)}{\sin \theta} \qquad [303]$$

The other components of magnetic field are zero.

It is interesting to compare these equations, which give the radiation pattern of a quarter-wave antenna, with the equations of radiation from a short antenna (equations 287 and 288). They turn out to be very similar. Both contain the same cosine function of time, although written in slightly different form. The peculiar trigonometric function in the numerator of equations 302 and 303, the cosine of the cosine of an angle, is numerically similar to the square of the sine of the angle; this function divided by $\sin \theta$ is therefore not greatly different from $\sin \theta$, the corresponding term in equations 287 and 288. It follows, therefore, that the radiation pattern of a quarter-wave antenna above a perfect ground is but slightly different from that of a short antenna if the same total power is radiated from both. (The horizontal radiation is some 6 per cent greater from the quarter-wavelength antenna than from a short antenna, with a corresponding decrease near vertical.) The radiation pattern of Fig. 51 is almost as suitable for a quarter-wavelength antenna above ground (or an isolated half-wavelength antenna) as it is for a very short radiator.

But if the length of the antenna above ground is much greater than a quarter wavelength the radiation pattern is radically altered. Up to about six-tenths of a wavelength the horizontal radiation is increased, and the radiation pattern becomes a long, low loop rather than a half-circle. Still longer antennas radiate upward at an angle, with a relatively weak ground wave. The proper choice of height (particularly on an economic basis) is very important in antenna design.

RECEIVING ANTENNAS. As an electromagnetic wave travels through space a changing magnetic field continually produces an electric field, and the resulting electric field continually reproduces a magnetic field. When the wave passes any given point in space the changing magnetic field induces an electric field at that point, and if the wave passes a wire of conducting material it induces an electric field in that wire.

There are two general ways to consider the action of the conductor as a receiving antenna. The most straightforward is to recognize that the passing wave will be distorted by the presence of conducting material; its electric and magnetic fields will be weakened because there can be no field strength within a perfect conductor. Current will flow in the conductor, providing proper termination for the electric and magnetic fields of the wave. From this point of view the receiving antenna is a boundary problem.

The alternative method is indirect, but it is more useful for practical computation. It assumes that electromotive force is induced in the antenna by the magnetic field of the *undistorted* passing wave, that as a result current flows, and that this current acts in the antenna as if it were a transmitting antenna and produces a new electromagnetic field that is superimposed upon the undistorted wave. The flow of current in this case is limited by the distributed capacitance and inductance of the conductor, and by its resistance (loss resistance) and " radiation resistance." The problem thus becomes a circuit problem and is much easier to handle.

We will divide radio receiving antennas into three classes for discussion, although any such classification is quite arbitrary. First we will consider a straight wire that is isolated from ground. Current flowing in such a wire will be charging current that can flow from end to end, limited by the capacitance of one end of the wire relative to the other. The conductor shown in Fig. 43, page 97, is an example, and in the alternating magnetic field of a wave there will be alternating current flowing from end to end of such an antenna at the frequency of the passing wave.

The electromotive force induced in the entire length of a straight wire that is short compared to the wavelength is the product of the length of the wire, the electric field strength of the wave, and the cosine of the angle between the wire and the electric vector. (In a longer wire it is necessary to take into account phase differences.) The *effective* electromotive force is less than this, however, for only an infinitesimal part of the antenna current flows all the way from one end of the wire to the other. The effective electromotive force depends upon the distribution of capacitance, and can be increased by increasing the capacitance near the end of the antenna.

In making use of an isolated straight wire as an antenna, a radio receiving apparatus is located at its midpoint. As much energy as possible is abstracted from the oscillating antenna current by the receiving apparatus. To increase the antenna current, inductance may be inserted as part of the receiving apparatus, providing resonance with the distributed capacitance of the antenna. The current that flows in such a " tuned " antenna is limited only by the energy lost in resistance and the energy reradiated from the antenna, for inductance and capacitance are balanced against each other. Tuning gives the optimum operation of an antenna. A tuned antenna can be considered as an oscillatory circuit; its voltage, from end to end, may be many times the electromotive force induced by the passing wave, for the induced electromotive force is merely enough to maintain the natural oscillation of the antenna current. An antenna one-half wavelength long is naturally tuned without the addition of inductance, for the distributed inductance of the wire itself just balances its distributed capacitance.

For practical computation it is possible to devise an equivalent circuit, in which an equivalent lumped voltage (representing the effective electromotive force of the antenna) drives current through an equivalent lumped antenna impedance in series with the impedance of the receiving apparatus.[1] Antenna design is based on an equivalent circuit of this kind.

An antenna in the form of a vertical straight wire with one end connected to ground will next be considered. Radio receiving apparatus is introduced into the antenna at the point of connection to ground. This

[1] For discussion of this and other engineering applications see *Radio Engineering*, F. E. Terman, Second Edition, McGraw-Hill Book Co., New York, 1937.

is the most familiar type of receiving antenna. It receives only the component of a passing wave that is polarized with the electric field vertical, but this is the usual polarization of a wave from an ordinary transmitting antenna. It is non-directional in a horizontal plane, for the directional characteristics of a receiving antenna are the same as those of the same antenna used for transmitting.

The operation of a grounded antenna is not essentially different from that of an isolated antenna of twice the length. Current is limited by the capacitance from antenna to ground, and the greater capacitance of a grounded antenna compensates for the lower electromotive force induced in its shorter length. The effective value of the induced electromotive force is increased, and the impedance of the antenna to ground is decreased, if there is a relatively large part of the capacitance to ground near the top of the antenna, and this is often provided by connecting horizontal wires at the top of a vertical conductor.

A loop antenna is the third form to require discussion. Its operation is not essentially different except that flow of current in the loop is not limited by capacitance but by inductance in series with the receiving apparatus. Electromotive force is induced in the loop in the same way that it is in any conductor; it is induced by the changing magnetic field and is equal to the integral of the induced electric field around the loop.[2]

---

[2] A question that very commonly arises in reference to receiving antennas is: Is the antenna voltage produced by the electric field of the passing wave, or the magnetic field, or both? This is a natural question, but the answer is clear when it is considered that *anywhere in space* the electric field of a traveling wave is the result of a changing magnetic field. The electric field induced in an antenna is likewise the result of the changing magnetic field, and whether one wishes to consider the electromotive force as the integral of the electric field of the wave in space (which it is) or as produced by the change of magnetic field (which it also is) is immaterial. The above question is analogous to asking whether a cork rising on the crest of a water wave is lifted by increasing pressure or by the higher water level; in wave motion there cannot be one without the other.

If, however, a receiving antenna is close to an electric disturbance of some kind, conditions are quite different. Near the source of the disturbance the induction fields predominate, and the radiation fields are negligible. The electric induction field emanates from near-by charge, as distinguished from the radiation field that is produced by changing magnetic field. An electrostatic shield will protect a loop antenna from the *induction field* of near-by disturbances, for, like an electrostatic field, the induction field will not penetrate a closed metal surface. But a shield (in the usual form of a pipe that contains the wires of the loop) will not appreciably decrease the amount of magnetic flux that passes through a loop and links with it when a wave is going by. If the shield could act as a short-circuited turn it would reduce the magnetic field linking with the loop, but a shield for a loop antenna is designed with an insulating section so that it will not carry current around the loop. Hence a radio signal is received on an antenna inside the shield although much of

Consider for simplicity a rectangular loop with the sides vertical and the top and bottom horizontal. A passing wave is polarized with the electric vector vertical. Electromotive force will be induced by such a wave in the vertical members of the loop, but there will be none in the horizontal members. If the voltages induced in the two vertical members are identical, there will be no current in the loop. This condition results when the plane of the loop is parallel to the plane of the wave. But if the loop is turned 90 degrees so that its plane is normal to the plane of the wave, and parallel to the direction of wave propagation, the voltages in the two vertical members will be somewhat out of phase. The oncoming wave will reach one side of the loop before it reaches the other. The total electromotive force around the loop will then be the difference of the two induced voltages, and not zero. If the loop is small compared with the wavelength of the received signal the induced electromotive force in either vertical member is proportional to the height of the loop; the phase difference between voltages in the vertical members is proportional to the width of the loop; the electromotive force around the entire loop is proportional to the product of height and width, and therefore to the area of the loop.

The same conclusion is reached from a slightly different point of view, although the essential principle is the same. Induced electromotive force in the loop may be considered proportional to the rate of change of magnetic flux linkages through the loop (equation 159). It is then immediately evident that the area of the loop is a controlling factor, and that the loop will receive a maximum signal when its plane is normal to the magnetic field of the wave.

Loop antennas commonly have more than one turn of the antenna wire, and the antenna voltage is proportional to the number of turns. It is quite simple to compute the voltage between the terminals of a loop antenna if no current is allowed to flow. But when current flows the distributed inductance is important; the resistance of the wire and reradiation from the loop, as well as the impedance of the receiving apparatus must be considered; and the computation of received current and voltage is no less complicated than for other antennas.

The use of a loop antenna for determining the direction of arrival of a signal, and hence the direction to the station transmitting the wave, is evident. Other types of directional antennas can be used for direction finding, but the loop is the most common.

---

the noise brought by induction from near-by disturbances is eliminated. Antennas other than loops cannot be shielded, for their operation depends on their capacitance to ground, which a shield would eliminate.

ANTENNA ARRAYS.   When an array of sending antennas is used it is
sometimes possible to gain a good deal of information by superposition
of the fields from the component radiating elements.   For example,
two vertical antennas that are excited in time quadrature and that are
located one-quarter wavelength apart, as in Fig. 52, will radiate in the
direction from the leading antenna to the lagging antenna, but not in

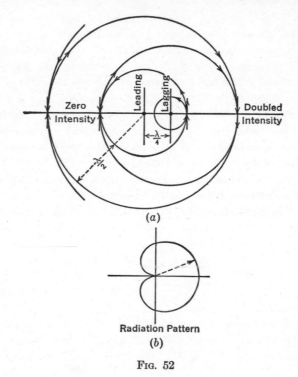

(a)

Radiation Pattern

(b)

FIG. 52

the opposite direction.   The reason is that a wave traveling from the
leading antenna to the lagging antenna will be reinforced by the wave
from the latter, for the quarter-cycle phase lead of the former wave will
just compensate for the quarter-cycle lead in space of the latter, while
the wave traveling from the lagging to the leading antenna will be a
half-cycle out of phase with the wave from the leading antenna and
hence the resultant field strength (at a considerable distance) in that
direction will be zero.   This is only one of many antenna arrays of
practical importance in obtaining desired radiation patterns.[3]

[3] A discussion of radio antennas, for which this chapter provides the theoretical
basis, will be found in Chapter XV of *Radio Engineering* by F. E. Terman.

A radiation pattern of particular interest is one that has a concentrated beam like a searchlight, with little energy spreading in other directions. A sharp beam can be achieved by using a very great number of radiating elements. If the radiating elements are so many and so close that they merge into a single conducting surface they become equivalent to a mirror. Indeed a single radiator at the focus of an actual mirror can be used to gain directivity with short radio waves just as with even shorter light waves.

Another way to gain directivity is to guide waves along a conducting surface. Spherical waves are unbounded; the waves of equations 287 and 288 fill all space and are everywhere consistent with Maxwell's equations without requiring any kind of termination. Plane waves, on the contrary, must be bounded, for they cannot practically extend to infinity with undiminished intensity. One way to bound a plane wave is to terminate its electric field upon a conducting wire, and a wave started along a wire must follow that wire to the end. This, as a matter of fact, is why wires are used in electric circuits. A wire is neither more nor less than a wave guide. Although this concept does not lead to a very tractable system of circuit analysis, it is most illuminating in connection with electric fields.

PROBLEMS

1. Compare the equations of this chapter with expressions for radiation field strength in another book, such as equation 222, Chapter XV, of *Radio Engineering* by F. E. Terman or equation 35, Chapter XIX, of *Communication Engineering* by W. L. Everitt.

2. Derive from equation 297 an expression for the radiated electric field of a short antenna above a perfect ground surface in terms of the actual height of the antenna and the current at the base of the antenna, using practical units.

3. Change equation 294 to express E_θ in microvolts per meter for radiation from a simple, short, vertical antenna above a perfect ground surface in terms of height, wavelength, and distance in meters, antenna voltage in volts, and frequency in cycles per second. Eliminate ω, l, and c.

4. Find the radiation resistance of a simple vertical antenna with a height of one-fourth wavelength above ground. Use an effective height of 0.6 times the actual height. Find the radiation resistance of a similar antenna if the radiated wavelength is 5.6 times the height. Use an effective height of 0.55 times the actual height. (See Ballantine "On the Radiation Resistance of a Simple Vertical Antenna," *Proc. Inst. Radio Eng.*, volume 12, 1924, pages 823–832.)

5. Show that equations 287 and 288 give the same value as is given by the exact equations 302 and 303 for *horizontal* radiation from a simple vertical antenna of height $\lambda/4$, erected above a perfect ground surface, if the effective height of the antenna is taken to be the actual height times $2/\pi$. Show that when computing *total* radiated power an effective height of 0.60 times the actual height (as in Problem 4) is a better value for a quarter-wave antenna, the correct radiation resistance

being 36.6 ohms. Explain this difference in the value of effective height to be used for different purposes.

6. A loop antenna 1 meter square, with ten turns of wire, is used to receive a radio signal. The signal is transmitted from a vertical antenna that rises to a height of 5 meters above ground. The wavelength is 50 meters. The receiving antenna is 10 kilometers from the transmitter, and is oriented for maximum reception. It is high above the ground surface. Find the signal strength at the receiver in microvolts per meter, and the open-circuit voltage of the antenna in microvolts.

CHAPTER XIII

WAVE GUIDES

GUIDED WAVES. When an electric wave is sent out through empty space it naturally becomes a spherical wave, for it travels with equal speed in all directions. There are no obstacles, and it can spread freely from its source. But the presence of material substance will affect its propagation.

As a sound wave is deflected by a rigid surface, an electric wave is deflected by any surface at which there is a change of electrical properties. The effect is marked when an electric wave encounters a highly conductive surface, for within conducting material an electric wave cannot exist. The ability of a conducting surface to act as the boundary of an electric wave is used in various kinds of wave guides for directing the propagation of electric waves, as the rigid wall of a speaking tube is used to guide sound by preventing the sound wave from spreading into space. A power line or a telephone line is a wave guide; the surface of the copper wire provides a boundary on which the electric field of a wave can terminate and the wave propagates as a plane wave, following the conductor from end to end. Because of the conducting wires the transmitted wave does not spread as a spherical wave but is able to travel as a plane wave, with all its energy directed along the route of the transmission line.

To show the need for a boundary surface, consider the plane wave of Fig. 46, page 114. This wave was described in Chapter X as extending without limit in a plane normal to its direction of travel. An unbounded wave like this is satisfactory from the mathematical point of view, but of course no physical wave can be of infinite extent. An actual plane wave must be held within finite limits.

It is possible to put thin sheets of perfectly conducting material into the region through which a wave travels without affecting the wave, provided they are everywhere normal to the electric field. If conducting sheets were parallel or oblique to the electric field, current would flow in them that would distort the field, but conducting planes that are normal to the field, as in Fig. 53, will not disturb it.

When conducting surfaces are placed in the field the electric lines of force will terminate on charge on the surfaces, and a plane wave can travel between such surfaces, and be limited to the space between them.   It is not necessary that the wave extend beyond the surfaces on either side.

Consider the lower surface of Fig. 53.   If a wave exists above it, but not below, as indicated, that surface must terminate the electric field and also the magnetic field.   Electric field can terminate only on electric charge (for elsewhere its divergence is zero), so there must be an appropriate distribution of charge on the surface.   Magnetic field can cease suddenly only at a surface carrying current (for elsewhere its curl is zero), so there must be current flowing in the surface of Fig. 53.

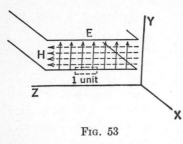

FIG. 53

These two requirements are not independent, for when the charge on the surface changes, as it must do to keep pace with the traveling wave, its motion constitutes current.   This does not mean that charge flows as fast as the electric wave travels — air molecules transmitting a sound wave do not flow with the speed of sound — but current flows from regions of decreasing charge density to regions of increasing charge density.

If the plane wave is to move between conducting surfaces in a normal and undistorted manner the currents flowing in the surfaces must accomplish these two requirements: they must at the same time provide necessary curl to act as a boundary for the magnetic field, and provide the proper distribution of charge to terminate the electric field at all times.   Let us see whether this is possible.

First, there is a definite relation between the electric field and the magnetic field of a wave, as defined by Maxwell's equations.   There cannot be a wave in free space unless

$$\nabla \times \mathbf{H} = \frac{1}{c} \frac{\partial \mathbf{E}}{\partial t} \qquad [198]$$

To apply this equation to the plane wave of Fig. 53 it should be expanded in rectangular coordinates.   Since H_x and H_y are both zero, and H_z does not vary with y, the expanded form reduces to

$$-\frac{\partial H_z}{\partial x} = \frac{1}{c} \frac{\partial E_y}{\partial t} \qquad [304]$$

The wave of Fig. 53 may vary as any desired function of time, but the electric and magnetic components will always be related by equation 304.

Second, the distribution of charge on the boundary surface is related to the electric field strength at that surface. Using σ to represent charge per unit area, the charge on the lower conducting surface of Fig. 53 must be

$$\sigma = \frac{E_y}{4\pi} \qquad [305]$$

As E changes with time the charge density will change. Consider some point on the conducting surface at which the charge density is increasing; charge is supplied to this point by current that flows parallel to the X axis. If the current conveying this charge is flowing in the positive X direction, and is a positive current, and provides positive charge, it will be a little smaller after it has passed the point in question and deposited thereon some of its positive charge. Quantitatively, the decrease of current with respect to distance x is equal to the increase of charge with respect to time. If I_x is current in the X direction in a strip of the conducting surface of unit breadth,

$$-\frac{\partial I_x}{\partial x} = \frac{\partial \sigma}{\partial t} \qquad [306]$$

Combining this[1] with equation 305, the necessary relation between changing electric field and flow of current is

$$\frac{\partial E_y}{\partial t} = -4\pi \frac{\partial I_x}{\partial x} \qquad [307]$$

This tells the amount of current necessary to terminate the electric field.

Third, the current in the conducting surface of Fig. 53 must be related to the magnetic field strength parallel to the surface. It can be considered that the changing magnetic field of the wave induces current in the conducting surface. A better mental picture results from consider-

---

[1] Equation 306 is a special case of the " equation of continuity " which may be derived as follows. From Maxwell's equations,

$$\nabla \times \mathbf{H} = \frac{1}{c}\left(4\pi \, \iota + \frac{\partial \mathbf{D}}{\partial t}\right)$$

Find the divergence of each side of this equation: on the left the divergence of the curl is identically zero; on the right, there results a term for the divergence of **D**. For the divergence of **D** substitute $\nabla \cdot \mathbf{D} = 4\pi\rho$. Then

$$4\pi \, \nabla \cdot \iota + \frac{\partial}{\partial t}(4\pi\rho) = 0$$

from which

$$\nabla \cdot \iota = -\frac{\partial \rho}{\partial t}$$

ing current as the boundary of a magnetic field. Experiment IX showed that

$$\oint \mathbf{H} \cdot d\mathbf{s} = \frac{4\pi}{c} I \qquad [167]$$

so that the integral of magnetic field around a closed path is related to the current linked by that path. If this equation is applied to a rectangular path of integration, as shown by a dotted line in Fig. 53, with sides parallel to the conducting surface each one unit long and with the upper side in the magnetic field while the lower is in field-free space, this equation becomes

$$H_z = \frac{4\pi}{c} I_x \qquad [308]$$

This tells us the current that must flow in the conducting surface to act as boundary for the magnetic field. H is in the positive Z direction, I in the positive X direction.

To compare this value with the current that is necessary to produce the proper electric field, we differentiate, obtaining

$$\frac{\partial H_z}{\partial x} = \frac{4\pi}{c} \frac{\partial I_x}{\partial x} \qquad [309]$$

By comparing equation 309 with 307, it appears that the same current will be satisfactory for terminating the electric field and for bounding the magnetic field if the electric and magnetic fields are related by

$$\frac{\partial H_z}{\partial x} = -\frac{1}{c} \frac{\partial E_y}{\partial t} \qquad [310]$$

But the electric and magnetic fields are always related in this manner, for this is identical with equation 304 derived from Maxwell's equation. The conclusion is that a wave *can* be limited to the space between two perfectly conducting parallel plane surfaces, since the current that flows in those surfaces will provide a proper boundary for both the electric and magnetic fields of the wave.

To avoid the necessity of repeating this proof for every conducting surface that acts as a wave guide, it can be shown to be true in general for all waves in which the electric vector is normal to a perfectly conducting surface. The proof is a generalization of the one given here for a plane wave, and shows that when an electric and a magnetic field are related by Maxwell's equations they are always properly terminated by the current that flows in a perfectly conducting surface normal to the electric field. Details of this proof will not be given, but the result may be accepted in our further discussion of wave guides.

It is possible for a traveling wave to be guided between curved conducting surfaces, and so carried around a corner. The radius of curvature should be large compared with the wavelength, for the process of getting around the bend is one of combined distortion and reflection as the electric field readjusts itself to be always normal to the conducting surfaces.

EFFECT OF LOSS. In the perfectly conducting material that is assumed for bounding surfaces, current will flow on the exact surface. There will be no penetration of current into the material. Electric and magnetic fields will both be terminated by an abrupt discontinuity at the surface. With a practical material, such as copper, current flows throughout the material, but it tends to be concentrated (especially at high frequencies) in a region *near* the surface. Both the electric and magnetic fields penetrate a short distance into the copper, and the changing magnetic field within the copper is the cause of current flow. The depth of penetration depends upon the rate of change of field strength; thus, in a sinusoidal wave it depends upon the frequency. This is " skin effect," and at low frequency the current is distributed practically uniformly through the thickness of conducting material whereas at high frequency it flows quite close to the surface.[2]

Since there is some loss of energy when current flows in copper, or in any practical material, the actual guided wave loses energy as it travels. Its intensity will gradually diminish. Also, because of the resistance of the material, the flow of current is never quite as great as it should be, and the consequence of this is that the wave is slightly bent back at the edges and its rate of propagation is delayed. The Poynting field of the wave is so directed that it has a small component into the copper. The velocity of the guided wave is slightly less than the velocity of light in free space.

Whenever a wave is traveling along a surface that is not perfectly conducting, as a wave within a guide travels along the metal surface, or as a radiated wave travels over the earth, the electric field is not exactly normal to the surface. The electric field is inclined forward, as if there were a drag in passing over the imperfectly conducting material. The Poynting vector is consequently inclined toward the surface, showing that the electric wave supplies energy consumed by current flow in the material.

This makes possible an important practical means of measuring

[2] A good discussion of skin effect is given in *Electric Power Transmission and Distribution*, L. F. Woodruff, John Wiley and Sons, New York.

ground resistance at radio frequency. The amount of energy consumed in the earth's surface when a wave passes over it depends on the earth conductivity; hence the angle of the electric vector is a measure of the conductivity. By using a directional receiving antenna to determine the slope of the electric vector in such a wave, the effective earth resistivity may be obtained.

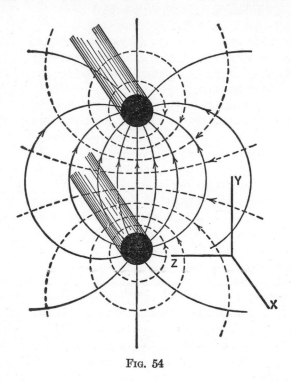

Fig. 54

FINITE WAVES. Although the wave of Fig. 53 is bounded in one dimension, it is still infinite in the other, and so it is not physically attainable. But the above discussion points the way to two types of wave guides that are actually useful.

Consider the lower conducting surface of Fig. 53 bent down and rolled into a cylinder, and the upper surface bent up, and rolled into a cylinder. The result will be as shown in Fig. 54; there will be parallel conducting cylinders serving as a wave guide for a plane wave. The lines of electric flux will be bent and stretched into arcs of circles, and the magnetic flux lines will curve about the cylindrical conductors in an orthogonal set of circles.

To show that these conductors, which comprise a parallel-wire transmission line, will act as a satisfactory wave guide it is only necessary to show that Maxwell's equations are satisfied in space between and around the conductors. This proof, although rather involved, is not difficult. For the simpler fields of a concentric transmission line the proof gives no trouble. See Problem 1, page 175.

A wave guided by parallel wires is infinite in extent, but its strength diminishes in all directions, and its energy is finite. It is therefore a physically possible wave. The physical wave on such a line, however, differs from the mathematical wave in one way: it must be generated at one place and terminated at another, and near the ends of the transmission line the wave is not a plane wave. It goes through some kind of a transition, from quasi-spherical wave to quasi-plane wave. A similar disturbance takes place if there is a change of direction of the line, or a change of diameter or spacing of the conductors. When the wave is not strictly a plane wave some energy is radiated away from the line, and goes out into space generally, instead of following the conductors. This lost radiation is negligible at power frequency; at radio frequency it may be of great importance.

When the cylindrical conductors do not have perfect conductivity the effect is much the same as discussed above for plane conductors. There is some penetration of current into the conductors; indeed, at low frequency, the current will penetrate the entire conductor. The speed of propagation is slightly less than the speed of light. The wave is not strictly a plane wave, but is bent back near the conductor. Indeed, transmission-line equations must be considered as merely good approximations except when applied to lines of zero resistance. (This is true even when line resistance and leakage are included in the equations.)

Most developments of transmission-line equations are based on the assumption that the capacitance and inductance of each short length of line may be considered independently of the rest of the line.[3] The assumption requires justification, for it is not apparent that there will be no electric or magnetic inductive effects between successive sections of the line. The justification is obtained in the proof outlined above: because the assumed electric and magnetic fields satisfy Maxwell's equations, they are correct. But this justification is obtained only with perfect conductors. If there is resistance the transmission-line equations obtained by that method are good and useful approximations, but not mathematically exact.

HOLLOW WAVE GUIDES. A suggestion of another type of wave guide is obtained from consideration of the parallel planes of Fig. 53. A

[3] This development is given (with an explanatory note) in *Transient Electric Currents*, H. H. Skilling, Chapter IX.

wave between two planes is restricted vertically, but not horizontally. But let us use two other conducting planes as side walls of a rectangular wave guide as in Fig. 55.

A difficulty is immediately encountered. There cannot be any tangential electric field at the surface of these planes because they are conducting. Therefore it is necessary to consider a wave in which the electric intensity, although everywhere vertical, diminishes to zero at the side surfaces of the guide. This is indicated in the diagram by decreased density of electric flux.

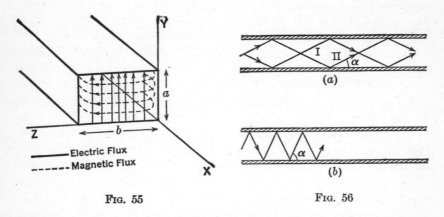

Electric Flux
Magnetic Flux

FIG. 55   FIG. 56

Such an electric field, because of its varying strength, has a component of curl along the X axis, and therefore requires an X component as well as a Z component of magnetic field. The resultant magnetic field is transverse at the middle of the wave guide, but it bends and becomes axial at the sides, as indicated by the dash lines in Fig. 55. The magnetic lines of flux form closed loops and the magnetic field is therefore without divergence, as indeed it must be.

The arrangement of electric and magnetic fields indicated in Fig. 55 cannot be produced by any single plane wave of the type that has been discussed in this and previous chapters, but it is rather surprising to find that it can be produced by two plane waves traveling within the wave guide at the same time. Neither of these waves goes axially along the guide, but each follows a zigzag path with multiple reflections from the walls of the guide as shown in Fig. 56a.

Only a sinusoidal wave will pass through a wave guide without distortion; let us therefore assume that waves I and II in Fig. 56a are sinusoidal waves. The angle at which they travel is dependent upon the wavelength and upon the size of the guide.

The essential point is this: two sinusoidal plane waves, of the same amplitude and frequency, when superimposed at an angle, will add to zero along certain surfaces.

Consider Fig. 57. Two waves are shown, one shaded black, the other white. They are traveling in somewhat different directions as shown by the arrows, the white wave almost directly away from the reader and the black wave toward the right. The waves are cut off at the near edge by a vertical plane through the dash line, the direction of which is midway between the directions of travel of the two waves. The intersection of the waves with this vertical plane gives the pair of sine curves that appear at the edge of the waves in the figure.

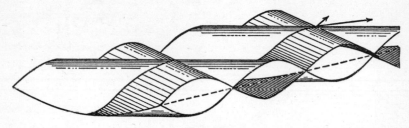

FIG. 57

The waves in this figure represent the electric intensity in two electromagnetic waves. Let the height of the pictured surfaces above or below the neutral plane be a representation of electric intensity. When the electric intensity of one wave is equal but opposite to the electric intensity of the other wave, the resultant electric intensity is zero. This is true all along the dash line, for where the black wave is above the dash line the white one is below by an equal amount and vice versa.

This is also the situation along another plane, parallel to the dash line, that cuts off the waves on the farther side. Along both of these planes the sum of the two waves is always exactly zero. At intermediate points the sum of the two waves is not zero, and the total resultant wave has the shape shown in Fig. 58, with a maximum value (where the black and white crests of Fig. 57 coincide) of twice the crest of either component wave alone.

Because the resultant electric field strength at the indicated boundary surfaces will always be zero, the pair of electromagnetic waves represented by the diagram may be contained within a rectangular wave guide of proper dimensions. They satisfy the requirement that there be no tangential component of electric field at a conducting surface: along the top and bottom of the guide the electric field is normal to the surface and along the two side walls it is zero. Both waves follow zigzag paths within the guide, as in Fig. 56, and are reflected back and forth from side to side. In fact, there is essentially but one wave, for each wave is the reflection of the other.

The total result is that a series of electromagnetic pulses go down the wave guide as in Fig. 58. This diagram shows the nature of the elec-

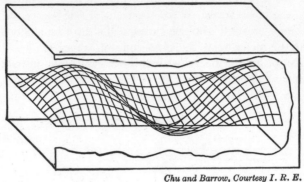

Chu and Barrow, Courtesy I. R. E.

FIG. 58

tric component of the wave, but it does not indicate the magnetic field. Figure 59 shows the distribution of both electric and magnetic components in this type of guided wave (known as the $TE_{0,1}$ wave).

GROUP VELOCITY. Waves in hollow guides have a number of peculiar properties and limitations. One is that the transmission of a radio signal along the tube will be at a speed somewhat less than the speed of light. This is easily explained in terms of the zigzag path followed

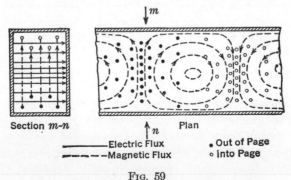

FIG. 59

by the two components, as shown in Fig. 56. Each plane-wave component travels at the speed of light along its zigzag path, but the rate at which a signal travels *along the guide* will be somewhat less because the zigzag path is longer than the axis of the guide. If a telegraphic dot or dash, or a telephonic modulation envelope could be observed, it would be seen to be going along the guide a little slower than the speed of light. Its velocity is known as the **group velocity**, v_g.

The group velocity of a wave in a guide is dependent upon its frequency. Consider crossed waves, as in Fig. 60, proceeding along a rectangular wave guide. (Note that lines in Fig. 60 indicate *crests* and not direction of travel of the waves. The direction of travel is normal to these crests. The appearance of this diagram is similar to Fig. 56, but the meaning of the crossed lines is exactly opposite.) For a given width of guide, the angle that the waves make with each other is determined by their wavelength. They must be crossed at such an angle that they overlap one wavelength in the width of the guide, as

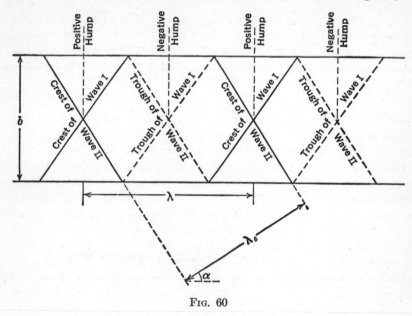

FIG. 60

in Fig. 60, thereby making the electric field zero at both conducting surfaces. The greater the wavelength of the component waves, the greater the angle; for a low-frequency wave the zigzag path will be squeezed up as in Fig. 56b, and group velocity will be relatively low. Finally, if the half-wavelength of the wave beomes as great as the width of the wave guide, the two component waves will be reflected back and forth across the guide, giving a standing wave, but there will be no forward progress at all. This is the **cut-off frequency** for the wave guide, and a wave of lower frequency cannot be transmitted because no wave of lower frequency can have zero electric field at both side walls of the guide.

The longest wavelength that can be transmitted along a rectangular guide with dimensions a and b as in Fig. 55 is therefore

$$\lambda_0 = 2b \qquad [311]$$

and the cut-off frequency is

$$f_0 = \frac{c}{2b} \qquad [312]$$

(This is based on the well-known relation between wavelength λ, velocity of propagation v, and frequency f, or angular velocity ω:

$$f = \frac{\omega}{2\pi} = \frac{v}{\lambda} \qquad [313]$$

Note that in equation 311 λ_0 is the cut-off wavelength of the *elementary* wave, or the wavelength that would be observed at the cut-off frequency in free space, and that correspondingly the velocity of propagation in free space, c, is used in equation 312.)

The group velocity of the $TE_{0,1}$ wave is

$$v_g = c \sqrt{1 - \left(\frac{\lambda_e}{2b}\right)^2} \qquad [314]$$

It is dependent upon λ_e, the wavelength of the elementary wave. It will be seen to approach zero as λ_e approaches $2b$, and to approach the speed of light for very short waves.

PHASE VELOCITY. Next let us consider the wavelength of the electromagnetic field within the wave guide. This will be the distance from hump to hump of Fig. 58, or the distance between the points of intersection of the crests of the two elementary waves in Fig. 57 or 60. Wave crests are indicated in Fig. 60; in this diagram the distance λ_e is the length of the elementary waves and λ is the apparent wavelength or the distance between humps of the total wave. The apparent wavelength is greater than the elementary wavelength.

Corresponding to this apparent wavelength is an apparent velocity greater than the speed of light. Consider the crossed crests of the two elementary waves as shown in Fig. 61. The solid lines show the present positions of the crests; the dash lines show their positions one unit of time earlier. The velocity is given by the distance through which the waves advance in this interval. At the point of intersection of the waves is the crest of the resultant or apparent wave. This point of intersection advances more rapidly than do the individual waves. The result is that if the wave pattern of Fig. 58 were visible it would appear to travel along the wave guide at a velocity greater than that of light. This apparent velocity is called the **phase velocity**, for it is the rate at which a given phase of the resultant wave travels.

It seems paradoxical that the waves should appear to travel in the guide at a speed greater than that of light, while a signal conveyed by those waves would go at the group velocity which is less than the speed of light. Yet that is what happens. Consider Fig. 62, which shows a " carrier " wave contained within a modulation envelope.[4] If it were visible in a wave guide the carrier wave would appear to be advancing at *phase velocity*, while the modulation pattern would progress at the

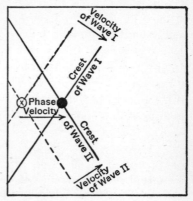

FIG. 61

slower *group velocity*.[5] The carrier wave would therefore seem to be slipping forward through the modulation envelope, and each individual crest of the carrier wave would change amplitude as it passed through the irregularities of the envelope until it disappeared entirely upon reaching the most advanced point of the envelope.

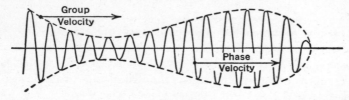

FIG. 62

The manner in which the apparent wave can pass out of existence is illustrated by Fig. 61. The wave crests in that figure come to an end toward the right. That may be considered the farthest point to which the signal has advanced. The apparent wave is the resultant of the two elementary waves, and appears as a hump at the point of intersection of the elementary waves; the hump advances rapidly from left to right until the elementary wave crests have passed beyond each other and no longer intersect, and then it simply disappears. Consider two

[4] Consider also, as a thoroughly non-mathematical example, a hurrying caterpillar. Little waves (transverse or compressional, depending on the species) ripple along its back from tail to head. These waves progress at phase velocity, while the caterpillar himself travels at group velocity.

[5] See " Note on Group Velocity and Phase Velocity," page 176.

waves traveling at an angle to each other on the surface of a body of water, and the disappearance of the double crest at their point of intersection is easily visualized.

An ocean wave, or a large wave on a lake, often approaches a retaining wall along the shore at a slight angle. Instead of advancing squarely upon the shore so that its full length breaks upon the wall at the same instant, the wave reaches the wall at one end a little sooner than it does at the other. When one watches such a wave there is a surge and splash at the point where the wave is breaking against the wall. This surge appears at one end of the wall with the first arrival of the wave, and then as the wave breaks progressively from one end of the wall to the other the surge (which marks the wave crest) appears to travel with great speed along the wall. Its speed may appear many times that of the actual rate of advance of the wave, and the less the angle between wave and wall the more rapidly it will seem to go. This apparent speed along the wall is a phase velocity, exactly analogous to the phase velocity in a wave guide.

The phase velocity of the $TE_{0,1}$ wave is given by

$$v_\phi = \frac{c}{\sqrt{1 - \left(\frac{\lambda_e}{2b}\right)^2}} \tag{315}$$

and it will be seen that the phase velocity is greater than the velocity of light in the same proportion as the group velocity is less. For very short waves the phase velocity, like the group velocity, approaches the speed of light, but at frequencies near cut-off the phase velocity approaches infinity.

Note particularly that a signal cannot travel at phase velocity, but only at group velocity.

DISTORTION. The previous discussion has been limited to the propagation in wave guides of sinusoidal waves of a single frequency. (Modulated waves require the presence of more than one frequency — of side bands as well as carrier — but the conclusions that have been reached are not significantly altered if the band of transmitted frequencies is narrow.) If waves of non-sinusoidal form are sent through a wave guide they are distorted as they travel. The reason is that any wave may be analyzed into sinusoidal components by Fourier analysis, and the fundamental and various harmonics (being of different frequencies) will travel at somewhat different speeds along the guide. The fundamental and harmonic components will therefore not have the same phase relation at the receiving end that they have at the sending end.

The total wave will be different in form. The general tendency will be for corners to be rounded and other distinguishing features of the wave to become blurred. This is not a matter of practical importance, however, for considering the order of magnitude of frequencies that can reasonably be sent in a hollow wave guide it will be seen that the propagated wave can serve only as a carrier for any purpose now conceivable.

DERIVATION. It is obvious that whether one looks upon the phenomena within a wave guide as a single wave or as a pair of zigzag waves, the electric and magnetic fields must be consistent with Maxwell's equations. A general solution of Maxwell's wave equations shows that waves of various patterns can be propagated within a guide of given form; let us, however, confine our attention to a wave of the kind shown in Fig. 55.

Since the electric field of this wave is parallel to the Y axis, the X and Z components may at once be set equal to zero as in equations 317 below.

The wave is assumed to be sinusoidal with respect to time, and since it is traveling along the X axis it will be described by a sinusoidal function of $(x - v_\phi t)$ where v_ϕ is its phase velocity. If its frequency is f, and $\omega = 2\pi f$, the electric field may be written as the following function of time:

$$\sin \frac{\omega}{v_\phi}(x - v_\phi t) = \sin(\beta x - \omega t) \tag{316}$$

In the latter expression $\beta = \dfrac{\omega}{v_\phi}$, and this defines β.

The electric field must be zero at $z = 0$ and at $z = b$. One way to accomplish this is to have a sinusoidal variation of electric field strength along the Z axis, starting at zero, rising to a maximum value at $b/2$, and falling again to zero at the side of the wave guide where $z = b$. With this sinusoidal space distribution, if the maximum strength of the field is A its strength at any value of z is $A \sin \dfrac{z}{b}\pi$.

Combining the variation-with-time and the variation-from-side-to-side-of-the-guide in a single equation

$$E_y = A \sin\left(\frac{z}{b}\pi\right)\sin(\beta x - \omega t)$$

and $$\tag{317}$$

$$E_x = 0$$

$$E_z = 0$$

EFFECT OF LOSS. So far it has been assumed that the wave guide is made of perfectly conducting material, so that there is no loss of energy and the wave is not attenuated as it travels. Actually this is impossible, and all waves are attenuated more or less.

If the frequency is only slightly greater than the cut-off frequency the attenuation is very rapid, for the elementary waves are reflected many times from the metal walls and at each reflection there is a loss of energy. At two or three times the cut-off frequency there is an optimum operating point with minimum attenuation. At still higher frequencies the loss rises again, but very gradually. This rising loss results from current in the guide walls on which electric field terminates; there must be charge in the walls to terminate the field and, as the field changes with the passing of the wave, current flows; the greater attenuation at high frequency results from increasing "skin effect," which increases losses slightly.

There are two walls of the guide on which no electric field terminates. They are required to carry current to serve as a proper boundary for the magnetic field. They carry a transverse current, with no component parallel to the axis of the guide, for only H_x exists at these surfaces. In the ideal case of perfectly conducting material, no magnetic flux penetrates these walls; the magnetic field abruptly becomes zero at the surface. But in the actual case there is just enough penetration of magnetic flux into the walls to induce electromotive force that produces the necessary flow of current to act as boundary for the magnetic field. This current, flowing in material that is not perfectly conducting, causes power loss. The character of the loss in these surfaces is such that it becomes continually less with increasing frequency. This is primarily because H_x (as in equation 323) becomes less at high frequency.

WAVE PATTERNS. The previous discussion has concerned one type of wave (the $TE_{0,1}$ wave) in a rectangular wave guide. Innumerable patterns of the electric and magnetic fields are possible within hollow guides, particularly when round guides as well as rectangular ones are considered. Several types of waves that give the greatest promise of practical value have been studied and described.[6]

[6] On the general subject of wave guides see: " Transmission of Electromagnetic Waves in Hollow Tubes of Metal," W. L. Barrow, *Proc. Inst. Radio Eng.*, volume 24, 1936, pages 1298–1328; " Transmission Theory of Plane Electromagnetic Waves," S. A. Schelkunoff, *Proc. Inst. Radio Eng.*, volume 25, 1937, pages 1457–1492; " Wave Guides for Electrical Transmission," G. C. Southworth, *Electrical Engineering*, volume 57, March, 1938, pages 91–95; " Waves in Hollow Tubes," L. J. Chu and W. L. Barrow, *Proc. Inst. Radio Eng.*, volume 26, 1938, pages 1520–1555; " Hollow Pipes of Relatively Small Dimensions," W. L. Barrow and H. Schaevitz, *Trans. AIEE*, volume 60, 1941, pages 119–122.

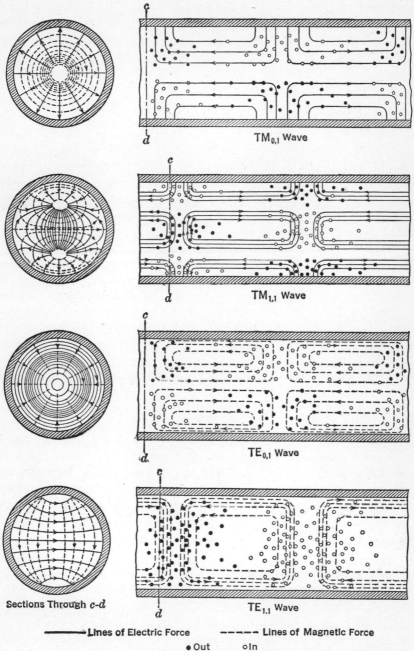

TM$_{0,1}$ Wave

TM$_{1,1}$ Wave

TE$_{0,1}$ Wave

Sections Through c-d

TE$_{1,1}$ Wave

———— Lines of Electric Force   - - - - - Lines of Magnetic Force

● Out   ○ In

G. C. Southworth, Bell Labs, courtesy Electrical Engineering

Fig. 63

One of the most remarkable is the $TE_{0,1}$ wave in a circular guide. In this particular wave, shown in Fig. 63, all electric flux lines as well as all magnetic flux lines are closed loops. None of the electric field terminates on charge on the walls of the guide. Consequently there is less current in the metal tube than for other types of waves, and there is correspondingly lower loss. Because none of the electric field terminates on the walls of the guide, the component of loss that increases with frequency (as discussed above) is entirely eliminated and this $TE_{0,1}$ wave has the remarkable and valuable peculiarity of being less attenuated as the frequency is increased indefinitely. (It is unfortunate, in view of this theoretical advantage, that experiment shows this wave to be unstable.)

Current in the cylindrical guide for the $TE_{0,1}$ wave circulates around the guide. There is no axial component of current along the guide. This seems queer to one accustomed to thinking of a transmission line as a means of conveying current. But when one thinks of a transmission line as a wave guide, and considers that current flows in the line only for the purpose of providing a boundary for the electric and magnetic fields, a new concept results.

From this point of view the difference between an open-wire transmission line and a hollow wave guide is that the electric and magnetic fields about the former extend outward, whereas in the latter the fields extend inward from the conducting surface. The concentric transmission line is an intermediate example. The conductors of all wave guides and transmission lines are for the purpose of carrying charge and current to terminate the fields and permit the existence of waves which, being guided, do not spread their energy uselessly through space.

Although a conducting surface is the best wave guide it is not the only possible kind. A dielectric surface will also serve as a boundary for certain types of waves. The discontinuity between material of high dielectric constant and low dielectric constant makes it possible to confine a wave within the material of high constant. The practical objection to the use of a dielectric wave guide is that the loss in all known dielectric materials is too great for satisfactory wave transmission.

The most suitable wave guide for any particular application depends on the conditions and particularly the frequency. At power frequency the parallel-wire transmission line is the best guide. At high radio frequency the concentric-conductor line is more desirable for, although more expensive to build, it has negligible radiation loss. Hollow wave guides do not have as high efficiency as concentric lines but they have other properties of great value. A section of hollow guide may be closed at the ends to act as an electromagnetic resonator, or a guide can be flared into a horn that will radiate ultra-high frequency waves with excellent directional characteristics. There is no doubt that all three types of wave guides will continue to be used.

PROBLEMS

1. A wave following a concentric transmission line, in which one conductor is a solid cylinder and the other a coaxial hollow cylinder, may be described in the empty space between the conductors as

$$E_r = \frac{E_0}{r} \sin \frac{\omega}{v} (z - vt)$$

$$E_\theta = E_z = 0$$

(a) This wave can exist only if the electric field has no divergence, and if it is a solution of the wave equation, equation 206. Determine whether these conditions are satisfied.

(b) From Maxwell's equations, determine the magnetic field of this wave.

(c) Find the current in the inner conductor, assuming perfect conductivity. Show that this current provides a proper boundary for both the electric and magnetic fields.

(d) Find the Poynting vector field.

(e) Find the velocity of the wave if the space between conductors is filled with oil, as in a power cable, of dielectric constant 2.17.

2. Relate the group velocity of a wave in a hollow rectangular guide to the angle between the paths of the elementary wave components and the axis of the guide. Call this angle α.

3. Find the angle α of Problem 2 in terms of the wavelength of the elementary wave component and the dimension b of the guide (see Fig. 60). From this derive equation 314.

4. Find the phase velocity from Fig. 61, and show that it may be expressed as equation 315.

5. A wave enters a wave guide with the form $E = E_m(\sin \omega t + \frac{1}{3} \sin 3\omega t)$. Plot the shape of the wave as it enters, and as it passes various positions along the guide. The cut-off frequency of the guide is half the frequency of the fundamental component of this voltage. Neglect attenuation.

6. Show that the divergence of the electric field described by equation 317 is zero in the space within the guide.

7. (a) Show that the divergence of the magnetic field of equation 323 is zero.

(b) Prove that the divergence of *any* magnetic field given by Maxwell's equation 199 will be zero.

8. If an oscillation of frequency less than the cut-off frequency of a wave guide is produced at the sending end of the guide it cannot produce a traveling wave within the guide. What will happen? Assume the walls of the guide to be perfectly conducting.

NOTE ON
GROUP VELOCITY AND PHASE VELOCITY

The difference between group and phase velocity in a wave guide can be explained in terms of elementary waves traveling with continual reflections. The wave guide is a special case, however, and it is not usually possible to account for group and phase velocity on the basis of component waves. The *general* condition is this: If the velocity of propagation of waves depends upon the wavelength, group velocity will differ from phase velocity.

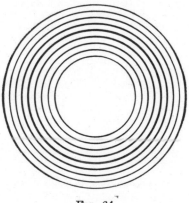

FIG. 64

The most familiar illustration is found in waves that spread over the surface of water. If a stone is dropped into a quiet pond a band of concentric circular ripples will travel outward from the point of disturbance. There will be a number of waves in the group, as in Fig. 64: the waves near the middle of the group will have the greatest amplitude, and the inner and outer waves will be vanishingly small. If one watches the waves with care the individual waves will be seen to travel faster than the group as a whole. A wave will appear at the inner circumference of the band and will gain amplitude as it moves outward, while other waves appear, one by one, behind it. After the wave has passed the middle of the band of waves, however, it will diminish in amplitude, until it becomes the outermost wave and finally vanishes. The individual wave moves with phase velocity; the band of waves moves with group velocity.

In Fig. 65 a cross section of such a band of waves is shown. It is indicated in the diagram that the band can be considered as the sum of two waves of constant amplitude but slightly different frequency. (This obviously corresponds to the analysis of a modulated radio wave into carrier frequency and side bands.) Two of the crests of the wave of shorter wavelength are marked 1 and 2; two crests of the wave of greater wavelength are marked a and b. The crests 1 and a coincide at the instant for which the diagram is drawn, and they add to give the greatest of the crests in the resultant wave, marked I. The position of the group of waves (that is, the position of the dotted envelope) is given by the position of this maximum crest.

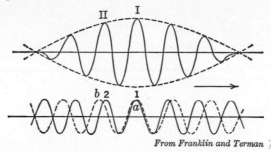

From Franklin and Terman

FIG. 65

Now assume that the wave in Fig. 65 is traveling from left to right, and that the nature of the medium is such that long waves travel a little faster (phase velocity) than short waves. At a slightly later instant of time crest b will overtake crest 2. When this happens crest a will have moved on beyond crest 1. Consequently, at this later instant (all waves having moved a considerable distance toward the right) the crest marked II will have become the maximum and central crest of the resultant group. Thus the center of the group of waves will have moved a lesser distance to the right (less by one wavelength) than the component waves of Fig. 65. The speed of the group of waves, known as group velocity, is therefore less (in this instance) than phase velocity.

Mathematically, the phase velocity of a wave is

$$v_\phi = \frac{\omega}{\beta} \qquad [324]$$

as in equation 316. It can readily be proved, although the proof will not be given here, that the group velocity is

$$v_g = \frac{d\omega}{d\beta} \qquad [325]$$

Therefore if β, the phase constant, can be expressed as a function of frequency and differentiated, the group velocity can be obtained. By this means equation 314 which gives group velocity in a wave guide can be obtained from phase velocity in equation 315 or 320.

Application of this formula to water waves shows that the phase velocity is twice the group velocity (if the waves are large enough to be independent of surface tension), as follows.

The phase velocity of water waves is known to be

$$v_\phi = \frac{g}{2\pi f} = \frac{g}{\omega} \qquad [326]$$

where g is acceleration due to gravity and f is frequency of the wave. It will be seen that high-frequency waves are propagated more slowly. From equation 324

$$\beta = \frac{\omega}{v_\phi} = \frac{\omega^2}{g} \qquad [327]$$

and differentiation gives

$$\frac{d\beta}{d\omega} = \frac{2\omega}{g}$$

whence

$$v_g = \frac{d\omega}{d\beta} = \frac{g}{2\omega} = \frac{1}{2} v_\phi \qquad [328]$$

as stated above.

It must be understood that when the wave motion is sinusoidal and steady, group velocity is not apparent. There are no groups; only individual waves can be observed, and they travel with phase velocity. If two frequencies are present, as in the illustration of Fig. 65, or three frequencies, such as the carrier and two side frequencies of a steadily modulated wave, the situation is fairly simple. But in a transient disturbance, such as the ring of waves that results from dropping a stone into water, or the short section of radio wave released as a telegraphic dot or dash, all frequencies are present. The result is then exceedingly difficult to analyze,[1] although it is qualitatively similar to the simple case.

To the electrical engineer the most familiar variation of velocity with frequency is on a transmission line with losses. If the resistance and leakage losses are not proportioned to give the " distortionless " condition, phase velocity of waves will be less than on the same line without losses. The phase velocity of low-frequency waves will be less than the phase velocity of high-frequency waves. Group velocity can

---

[1] See, for instance, *Communication Networks*, Volume II, E. A. Guillemin, John Wiley and Sons, New York, 1935.

be computed from phase velocity. On an ordinary transmission line group velocity will always be *greater* than phase velocity.[2]

Phase velocity of radio waves in the ionosphere is dependent upon frequency. The effect, in this case, results from vibratory motion of electrons in the ionized layer and reradiation of energy in slightly different phase. The net result is a phase velocity greater than the velocity of light, and group velocity less than the velocity of light. The group velocity can be quite low, and this is believed by some to account for the occasional observation of signals that reach a radio receiving station as much as several seconds later than they would have arrived if they had been propagated at the speed of light in free space.

Another example of variation of phase velocity with frequency is the propagation of light through transparent material. In glass, for example, high frequencies (blue light) travel more slowly than low frequencies (red light). One result of this action is the well-known dispersive effect of prisms. Phase and group velocities are both less than the speed of light in free space, and except in special cases the group velocity is less than the phase velocity.

[2] See E. A. Guillemin, *loc. cit.*

BIBLIOGRAPHY

Books

WOODS, F. S., *Advanced Calculus*, Ginn and Co., Boston, 1934.

PIAGGIO, H. T. H., *Differential Equations*, G. Bell and Sons, London, 1937.

COFFIN, J. G., *Vector Analysis*, John Wiley and Sons, New York, 1909.

SPIELREIN, J., *Lehrbuch der Vektorrechnung*, Konrad Wittwer, 1926.

PAGE, L., and ADAMS, N. I., *Principles of Electricity*, D. Van Nostrand Co., New York, 1931.

PIERCE, G. W., *Electric Oscillations and Electric Waves*, McGraw-Hill Book Co., New York, 1920.

ABRAHAM, M., and BECKER, R., *Classical Electricity and Magnetism*, G. E. Stechert and Co., New York, 1932.

MASON, MAX, and WEAVER, WARREN, *The Electromagnetic Field*, University of Chicago Press, Chicago, 1929.

PLANCK, MAX, *Theory of Electricity and Magnetism*, The Macmillan Co., London, 1932.

GUILLEMIN, E. A., *Communication Networks*, Volume II, John Wiley and Sons, New York, 1935.

FRANKLIN, W. S., and TERMAN, F. E., *Transmission Line Theory*, Franklin and Charles, Lancaster, Pa., 1926.

SKILLING, H. H., *Transient Electric Currents*, McGraw-Hill Book Co., New York, 1937.

Handbook of Engineering Fundamentals, John Wiley and Sons, New York, 1936.

Handbook of Chemistry and Physics, Chemical Rubber Publishing Co., Cleveland, Ohio.

ALBERT, A. L., *Electrical Communication*, John Wiley and Sons, New York, 1934.

EVERITT, W. L., *Communication Engineering*, McGraw-Hill Book Co., New York, 1937.

TERMAN, F. E., *Radio Engineering*, McGraw-Hill Book Co., New York, 1937.

Periodicals

BALLANTINE, STUART, " On the Radiation Resistance of a Simple Vertical Antenna at Wave Lengths Below the Fundamental," *Proc. Inst. Radio Eng.*, Volume 12, 1924, pages 823–832.

BALLANTINE, STUART, " On the Optimum Transmitting Wave Length for a Vertical Antenna over Perfect Earth," *Proc. Inst. Radio. Eng.*, Volume 12, 1924, pages 833–839.

BARROW, W. L., " Transmission of Electromagnetic Waves in Hollow Tubes of Metal," *Proc. Inst. Radio Eng.*, Volume 24, 1936, pages 1298–1328.

SCHELKUNOFF, S. A., " Transmission Theory of Plane Electromagnetic Waves," *Proc. Inst. Radio Eng.*, Volume 25, 1937, pages 1457–1492.

SOUTHWORTH, G. C., " Wave Guides for Electrical Transmission," *Electrical Engineering*, Volume 57, March, 1938, pages 91–95.

CHU, L. J., and BARROW, W. L., " Waves in Hollow Tubes," *Proc. Inst. Radio Eng.*, Volume 26, 1938, pages 1520–1555.

BARROW, W. L., and SCHAEVITZ, H., " Hollow Pipes of Relatively Small Dimensions," *Trans. A.I.E.E.*, Volume 60, 1941, pages 119–122.

INDEX